Exploring Energy Choices

We did this preliminary report in the hope of helping citizens understand the energy issue.

Pamela Baldwin, research associate
Monte Canfield, Jr., project deputy director
Steven Carhart, technology assessor
Evelyn Chisholm, secretary
Shirley Cox, secretary
John Davidson, physicist
Norma Dosky, secretary
Joy Dunkerley, economist
Charles Eddy, lawyer
Frances Francis, economist
S. David Freeman, project director
Katherine Gillman, writer
Lucille Larkin, public information specialist
Sharon Lynn, staff assistant
Arjun Makhijani, engineer
Valeria Moore, secretary
Shelley Prosser, librarian
Kenneth Saulter, economist
Majester Seals, administrative specialist
David Sheridan, editor
Billie Truesdell, secretary
J. Frederick Weinhold, engineer
Robert Williams, physicist

EXPLORING ENERGY CHOICES

A Preliminary Report of the
Ford Foundation's
Energy Policy Project

**This paper is 100% recycled from waste paper.
No virgin fibers were used in its manufacture.**

Contents

Foreword

In December 1971, the Trustees of the Ford Foundation authorized the organization of the Energy Policy Project. In subsequent decisions the Trustees have approved supporting appropriations to a total of $4 million, which is being spent over a three-year period for a series of studies and reports by responsible authorities in a wide range of fields. The Project Director is S. David Freeman, and the Project has had the continuing advice of a distinguished Advisory Board chaired by Gilbert White.

This preliminary report is the Project's first published product. It is an interim statement, designed, as its introduction says, to "invite comment, criticism and suggestions." Indeed it contains such comment from four members of the Project's own Advisory Board.

The fact that this report is preliminary does not make it unimportant. The problems of energy policy are large and hard, and most public analyses address a limited segment of the problem or argue from the standpoint of a particular interested party. Both kinds of study are important, but neither is a substitute for a broader effort to set the issues of national policy in a general framework which can assist citizens and their representatives in reaching balanced judgments.

The Energy Policy Project has been carefully designed at once to avoid control by any special interest and to enlist the advice and counsel of many different kinds of experts. As this first report explains, the Project's leaders have commissioned studies of a number of specific problems where previous analysis has been conspicuously incomplete. They have also set out to frame some of the basic alternatives before this country in ways which will help in the hard work of informed democratic choices.

I believe this preliminary report is an important first step in the Project's work. I do not presume to pass judgment for the Ford Foundation on the specific conclusions which are advanced herein, either in the report itself or in the comments of members of the Advisory Board, but I do believe that both the report and the comments are useful contributions to public understanding. This country will be discussing these hard issues for a long time to come, and the energetic and open expression of varied views will be needed more and more. Both the leaders of the Project and the members of the Advisory Board have earned by their experience and effort the right to be carefully heard.

McGeorge Bundy
President, Ford Foundation

Introduction

The Ford Foundation's Energy Policy Project was established two years ago to explore the whole complex of energy issues facing the nation. In the meantime the rush of events has thrust the energy crisis to the center of the nation's attention and given our work an added sense of urgency. Coordinating the Project is an interdisciplinary staff of economists, engineers, scientists, writers and lawyers located in Washington, D.C., assisted by a number of outside consultants. The staff is responsible for much of the Project's task of fact-finding and analysis. In addition, the Project has commissioned two dozen major research studies and many more smaller ones from independent energy experts across the nation to help provide important pieces of the energy puzzle. Preliminary drafts of most of the research reports have been completed and are being reviewed by outside experts.

Throughout our work, the Project has benefited from the counsel of an Advisory Board, made up of distinguished persons from business, academia and citizen groups. Advisory Board comments on this report appear on p. 55. (Members of the Energy Policy staff are listed on the inside of the front cover and of the Advisory Board in Appendix A).

This report is the first publication of the Energy Policy Project. Our work is not yet complete, but we believe that a preliminary overview is timely. As a first report, it does not contain detailed information or analyses of particular issues but rather seeks to provide a framework for thinking about energy policy. We have developed an approach to energy problems which attempts to fit together diverse energy issues in a coherent way. We hope that this approach will be useful to the public at a time when important energy decisions, whose consequences will be with us for a long time, are being taken.

Our major tool for analyzing energy policy options is to set forth three descriptions, or scenarios, of the future. Section 7 of this report provides the highlights of these scenarios based on our research so far. It is not our purpose to advocate a particular option, or even to suggest that these three are the only options. We hope that publication of our preliminary analysis, even though it is tentative, will invite comment, criticism, and suggestions that can be reflected in our final report. Our intention is to contribute to the energy policy dialogue in a timely fashion and to elicit a response that will strengthen our final report.

This preliminary report also establishes a framework for the Project's publications of the special studies we have commissioned and the Project's own final report. Beginning in April, we will publish most of the special research studies, as they are completed, in a series of books (Ballinger Publishing Company). A list of the research studies undertaken for the Project by independent groups and scholars appears in Appendix B.

These studies will set forth the views of the research authors. The subject matter covers a spectrum varying from oil spills and their effects and prevention to a detailed analysis of energy taxes and subsidies. We designed our research to concentrate on selected issues that we saw as crucial to policymaking, but that lacked fresh analysis. For example, we sponsored a study by the National Academy of Sciences on *The Rehabilitation Potential of Western Coal Lands* because it is a major policy issue for which no impartial scientific analysis was available.

Another consideration in selecting research topics was whether an important issue was already in the spotlight or was relatively neglected. For instance, we selected for special study the issue of safeguarding nuclear material against theft but not the question of nuclear power plant safety, which has received intensive attention by others.

This Project is essentially a study of U.S. energy policy, but we do recognize that U.S. policy must reflect conditions in the rest of the world. One of our special reports will be a major study of the international aspects of U.S. energy policy, prepared by the Brookings Institution. Our study concentrates on one piece—the U.S. piece—of a world-wide problem which can be resolved only with full recognition of how interdependent the energy world has become.

Our staff will integrate the research work sponsored by the Project together with its own research, into a final report which will set forth this Project's analysis of the nation's energy options and their impact on prices, foreign policy, reliability of supply, the environment, and social equity.

The final report will present a comprehensive picture of three alternative scenarios of the future which are sketched briefly in this report. It will compare the advantages and drawbacks of each option, and will point out the policy actions appropriate to each. The final report will complete the Project's series of books in the last half of 1974.

No single study of energy policy can hope to present a definitive treatment of what has become a central concern of mankind. Yet, we hope this introduction to our work and the volumes that follow will provide a perspective that will help both citizen and decisionmaker better understand the energy issues in today's lively debate.

S. David Freeman
Director, Energy Policy Project

Exploring Energy Choices

SECTION 1

The Energy Gap

ENERGY PROBLEMS HAVE been brought forcefully to public view by the Arab embargo of oil sales to the United States, but the roots of our energy troubles go back to trends in production and consumption of energy that have persisted for some time. The first and most fundamental energy problem we face is a growing gap between growth rates in consumption and domestic production. Total energy use in the United States has more than doubled since 1950, while population has grown by only slightly more than one-third. From 1950 to 1973, U.S. energy consumption increased at an average annual growth rate of 3.5 percent, while domestic production rose more slowly at just under 3 percent. In the eight years after 1965, consumption raced ahead at 4.5 percent a year; but since 1970 growth in domestic production has been at a virtual standstill. By 1973, annual energy use in the United States had reached 75 quadrillion Btu's,* but production from native sources was only 62 quadrillion Btu's.[1]

In recent years imported fuel, primarily oil, has made up the difference between U.S. production and consumption. In slightly more than two decades the United States changed from a net exporter

* A Btu is the amount of energy needed to raise one pound of water by one fahrenheit degree. Energy from all fuels can be converted to Btu's. Conversion rates are approximately as follows:

1 42-gallon barrel of oil	=	5.8 million Btu's
1 cubic foot of natural gas	=	1,031 Btu's
1 kilowatt hour of electricity	=	3,413 Btu's
1 ton of coal	=	25 million Btu's

Following U.S. practice, we define quadrillion as 10^{15}.

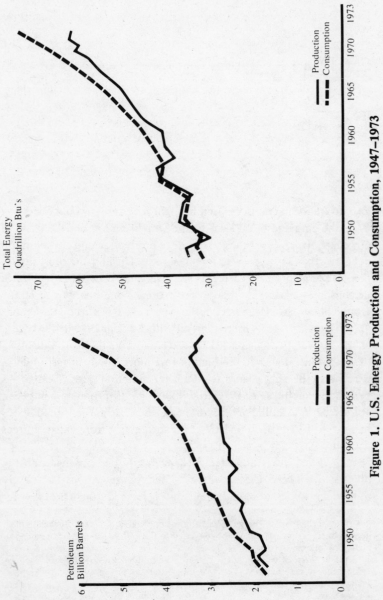

Figure 1. U.S. Energy Production and Consumption, 1947–1973

Note: Petroleum consumption includes natural gas liquids.
Source: U.S. Bureau of Mines

2

of energy to an importer of about 15 percent of its energy, including 35 percent of its oil. Figure 1 illustrates the growing gap between U.S. energy production and consumption and the even larger gap within the petroleum sector.

Energy Consumption

Energy consumption in the United States has been higher than in other nations for many years, but the rest of the world is growing even faster than we are in energy use. While our own use of energy has been rising at slightly more than 4 percent annually, world energy use has increased by 6 percent per year. Figure 2 shows U.S. energy consumption as a percentage of world consumption and indicates the downward trend since 1925. Even so, we still consume a third of the world's energy, with only 6 percent of its population.[2]

Abstract energy consumption figures can be traced to people, houses, appliances, vehicles and manufactured goods. A number of different trends in each energy use sector—residential, commercial, industrial and transportation—have contributed to rapid U.S. energy growth in the last decade.

Residential Energy Use

Population growth during the 1960s contributed to residential energy growth, but it was only one of several factors. While the population increased by about 11 percent, the number of households grew by 17 percent[3]—reflecting a tendency toward smaller households and a switch among elderly and young adults toward living in their own homes. In contrast, residential energy use increased by 50 percent. Residential energy growth also reflects greater affluence. Air conditioning, clothes drying, refrigeration and "other" (primarily lighting, television and assorted appliances) led the growth in household energy consumption in the decade of the 1960s. Table 1 illustrates this growth.

Preliminary data from an Energy Policy Project-funded study of energy and lifestyles[4] indicate that almost all American homes now contain five basic energy-consuming items: central heat, hot water heater, stove, refrigerator and electric lights. Virtually all have one radio and one television as well. Seven out of ten have washing machines. So-called "luxury" items (which may be considered necessities in some climates and circumstances) are less predominant but are

3

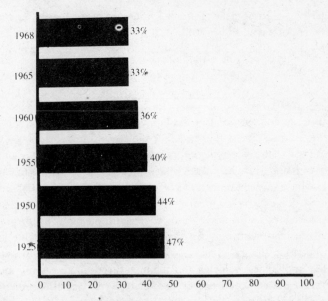

Figure 2. U.S. Energy Consumption as a Percentage of World Energy Consumption, Selected Years: 1925–1968.

Source: Sam Schurr, ed., *Energy, Economic Growth and the Environment.*

growing more rapidly in saturation. Central air conditioning, for example, grew from 5 percent of American households in 1969 to 15 percent in 1973. Dishwashers increased from 6 percent to 25 percent of all households during the same period. Clothes dryers, which existed in less than one-fifth of American households in 1960, were found in almost half by 1973.

In some cases, household energy growth has been further stimulated by design changes that diminish the efficiency of energy use. Most refrigerators now on the market are large, frost-free models requiring about two-thirds more energy per unit than smaller models needing manual defrosting. Color televisions typically consume almost half again as much electric power as black and white sets. Sometimes the growth of energy in one place has ripple effects. For example, dishwashers and automatic washing machines not only use electricity themselves, but also require even more energy for hot water heating.

Residential energy consumption levels are frequently influenced by decisions in which an individual homeowner has little to say.

Refrigerators, dishwashers, air conditioners and hot water heaters are often chosen by the builder, or by an owner who sells his house to new owners long before the appliances complete their life spans. Home heating systems are replaced even less often than appliances, so it is less likely that a current fuel consumer participated in the choice of systems. One-fifth of all American households (mostly apartment dwellers) have no control over their thermostat settings. Such residents can exert direct control over their dwelling temperatures only by opening windows or turning on portable electric heaters or electric blankets. This can add still more to their energy consumption.

The trend toward built-in energy-consuming features in new homes has grown in the last few years. Builders are incorporating electric heating systems and central air conditioning in an increasing number of homes and apartments, and concrete slab construction—without a basement to insulate the interior from the cold ground—is becoming more common.

Well-to-do families* can better afford to invest in energy-conserving devices such as insulation and storm windows, and their homes tend to have them. While only one-fifth of all single-family American homes have no insulation at all, half of the single-family homes of the poor** are without it. However, the insulated homes of high-income households still account for more energy use than the uninsulated homes of the poor, because they are larger and full of energy-consuming amenities. Suburban households use more energy than either urban or rural ones, and families living in single-family houses use more Btu's than those living in apartments.

Commercial Energy Use

The commercial sector includes such diverse institutions as stores, office buildings, hotels, service stations, schools, hospitals, theatres, restaurants and sports arenas. Commercial energy use has grown at the rate of 5.4 percent per year since 1960. (See Table 1.) Its rapid growth rate reflects the growth of commercial and service

* Families with annual incomes of $16,000 or more regardless of family size. (Washington Center for Metropolitan Studies).
** Families who fall into one of the following categories:
—1 or 2 persons, annual income of $3000 or below;
—3 or 4 persons, annual income of $5000 or below;
—5 or 6 persons, annual income of $7000 or below;
—7 or more persons, annual income of $9000 or below.
(Washington Center for Metropolitan Studies).

Table 1. Total Fuel Energy Consumption in the United States by End Use

End use	Consumption (trillions of Btu)		Annual rate of growth (%)	Percent of national total	
	1960	1968		1960	1968
Residential					
Space heating	4,848	6,675	4.1	11.3	11.0
Water heating	1,159	1,736	5.2	2.7	2.9
Cooking	556	637	1.7	1.3	1.1
Clothes drying	93	208	10.6	0.2	0.3
Refrigeration	369	692	8.2	0.9	1.1
Air conditioning	134	427	15.6	0.3	0.7
Other	809	1,241	5.5	1.9	2.1
Total	7,968	11,616	4.8	18.6	19.2
Commercial					
Space heating	3,111	4,182	3.8	7.2	6.9
Water heating	544	653	2.3	1.3	1.1
Cooking	93	139	4.5	0.2	0.2
Refrigeration	534	670	2.9	1.2	1.1
Air conditioning	576	1,113	8.6	1.3	1.8
Feedstock	734	984	3.7	1.7	1.6
Other	145	1,025	28.0	0.3	1.7
Total	5,742	8,766	5.4	13.2	14.4

Industrial				
Process steam	7,646	3.6	10,132	17.8	16.7
Electric drive	3,170	5.3	4,794	7.4	7.9
Electrolytic processes	486	4.8	705	1.1	1.2
Direct heat	5,550	2.8	6,929	12.9	11.5
Feedstock	1,370	6.1	2,202	3.2	3.6
Other	118	6.7	198	0.3	0.3
Total	18,340	3.9	24,960	42.7	41.2
Transportation					
Fuel	10,873	4.1	15,038	25.2	24.9
Raw materials	141	0.4	146	0.3	0.3
Total	11,014	4.1	15,184	25.5	25.2
National total	43,064	4.3	60,526	100.0	100.0

Note: Electric utility consumption has been allocated to each end use.

Source: Stanford Research Institute, *Patterns of Energy Consumption in the United States*, prepared for the Office of Science and Technology, Executive Office of the President, 1972.

activities themselves which have outpaced industrial growth consistently over the last decade.

Most of the energy used in the commercial sector is consumed for space heating and cooling, for lighting and for office equipment. Office buildings built in recent years use far more energy, on the average, than do older buildings with an equivalent amount of space. The difference can be traced to higher lighting levels, sealed windows (requiring twenty-four-hour mechanical ventilation), glass curtain walls (allowing high levels of heat loss and gain), and to proliferation of computer, elevators, escalators, electric typewriters and duplicating machines.[5] More research work is needed to determine the precise quantitative effects of these features on energy consumption, and to suggest opportunities for reducing commercial energy needs through conservation programs.[6]

Transportation Energy Use

Eight out of ten American households now own at least one car, as do half of all poor households. Three in ten families have two cars, and one in ten has three or more.[7] Total vehicle miles driven in the United States have doubled every 15 years since 1940, reaching 1.2 trillion in 1972.[8] Figure 3 illustrates the long-term growth in vehicle miles, which is primarily responsible for the 4.3 percent annual growth in transportation energy since 1960. (See Table 1.)

Transportation energy growth also comes from reduced efficiency. There has been a general shift in both passenger and freight transport toward modes that consume more energy per passenger mile. Automobiles consumed an average of 8,100 Btu's per passenger mile in urban travel in 1970, while urban mass transit consumed less than half that amount.[9] Yet public transportation use has steadily declined. Automobiles account for over 95 percent of all urban passenger traffic.

In 1958, the average American car got over 14 miles per gallon; by 1973, the rate had dropped to less than 12.[10] The main reason has been the increase in auto weight. Fuel consumption and auto weight are directly related: a 5,000-pound car uses twice as much gasoline as a 2,500-pound car.[11] Each model car has crept upward in weight over the years. 1974 "intermediate" size cars, for example, weigh about the same as 1972 "full-sized" models.[12] Other factors contributing to a loss in fuel economy are air conditioning, power steering, automatic transmission and emission control devices. The fuel economy penalty due to emission control is about 10 percent on 1973 and 1974 models (compared with pre-control models—1967 and earlier), and other accessories have decreased gas mileage by another 10 percent to 12 percent.[13]

Automobiles also carry about 85 percent of all inter-city passenger traffic, while railroads and buses—the most energy-efficient modes —carry only 3 percent of the traffic. Airplanes consume even more energy per passenger mile than automobiles, and they are the fastest-growing mode of inter-city passenger transport. The air share of inter-city passenger travel increased from 4 percent in 1960 to 10 percent in 1970, when planes consumed 22 percent of the energy in this category.

In freight transportation, the trend has been the same. Rail transport is four times as efficient* as truck transport and 63 times as efficient as air transport, yet railroads are losing freight traffic to trucks and planes.

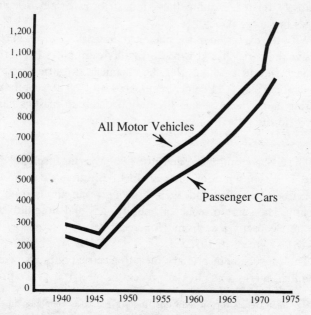

Figure 3. Growth in Vehicle Miles: 1940–1972 (billions)

Source: Motor Vehicle Manufacturers Association

* Measured as Btu's per ton-mile.

Industrial Energy Use

Industry uses more energy than any other consuming sector. In 1972, American industries consumed 30,000 trillion Btu's of fuels, or slightly over 40 percent of all energy consumed in the United States for that year. About half of that energy went for heating processes, either through direct burning of fuels or through the manufacture of steam.[14] Much of the rest was used for running machinery, electrolysis, lighting and for "non-energy" purposes—that is, as raw materials, or feedstocks, for manufacturing processes.

About 77 percent of all energy used in manufacturing feeds six highly consumptive industrial groups—food processing; paper; chemicals; petroleum refining; stone, clay and glass products; and the primary metals (particularly aluminum and steel).[15] In the case of food processing, the high energy consumption can be attributed simply to the size of the industry, rather than to energy-intensiveness.** For the other five groups, high consumption and energy-intensiveness are closely related, making these industries especially sensitive to changes in energy policy.

With the exception of the chemical industries, output in energy-intensive industries has grown less rapidly during the 1960s than in manufacturing as a whole. But the chemical industries grew at an annual rate of almost 11 percent compared with 7.9 percent for manufacturing as a whole.[16] Thus the nation's shift to plastics has contributed to the growth of industrial energy use.

Electricity

The U.S. consumption of electric power has far surpassed growth in the direct consumption of fossil fuels. Electricity use more than doubled between 1960 and 1970, growing at an annual rate of 7.4 percent.[17] The share of coal, oil, natural gas and uranium used to generate electricity rose from 15 percent of primary energy use in 1960 to 25 percent in 1972.[18]

The conversion of primary fuels to electricity always involves a substantial energy loss. In the process of electrical generation and

---

** Energy-intensiveness for an individual industry, such as aluminum smelting, is defined as the ratio of Btu's consumed to the dollar value of other direct costs, especially capital, labor and raw materials (which together are referred to as "value added"). While the average manufacturer consumes 60,000 Btu's per dollar of value added, the energy-intensive industries referred to above consume an average of over 200,000 Btu's per dollar of value added.

Table 2. Imports of Crude Oil and Refined Products 1960–1973

Year	Imports (thousands of barrels per day)	Imports (percent of total oil demand)
1960	1,815	18.1
1965	2,468	21.1
1970	3,419	22.8
1972	4,741	28.6
1973	6,100*	35.

Sources: U.S. Bureau of Mines; Independent Petroleum Association of America, "Summary of Statistics," *Supply & Demand Outlook,* December 1973.

*Preliminary estimate from *International Economic Report of the President,* February 1974.

transmission, about 65 percent of the energy content of the fuel is lost.[19] When there is a choice between burning fossil fuels directly or using electricity—as in home heating—direct fuel use is generally more efficient and less expensive. But electricity has the advantage of flexibility, since any fuel can be used for generation, and plentiful fuels can be substituted for scarce ones. Electricity is the only form in which atomic energy can be used.

Energy Supplies: Oil

Within three years after World War II, domestic petroleum was plentiful. In the 1950s, however, a much lower-cost source of oil became available in the Middle East. The fantastic productivity of Middle Eastern fields made costs there so low that Middle East crude oil could be delivered to the United States more cheaply than crude from domestic fields, even including transportation costs. To protect the U.S. oil industry's economic position in the domestic oil market, and to prevent over-reliance on foreign oil subject to cutoff in time of international strife, oil import quotas were established by President Eisenhower in 1959 and maintained until 1973.

During the 1960s, despite the quotas on imported oil—some would say because of the quotas—the nation's comfortable position with respect to domestic oil supply deteriorated. Exploration declined and major new oil finds were limited to a few offshore areas and the North Slope of Alaska. Toward the end of the decade, environmental concerns emerged, particularly after the Santa Barbara oil spill of

1969, and offshore leasing was virtually halted for 17 months. Concurrently, production of many older U.S. fields began to peak out, so new domestic wells served primarily as replacements for older wells, rather than as suppliers to meet growth. Imports have supplied our growth needs since 1970.

Oil imports have tripled since 1960. By 1973, 35 percent of total oil demand was imported, one-third in the form of residual fuel oil. Table 2 illustrates the growth of imports since 1960.

Traditionally, the bulk of U.S. petroleum imports have come from Venezuela and Canada with smaller amounts coming from the Middle East, North Africa, Nigeria and Indonesia. In the past two or three years, the fraction of petroleum originating from the Middle East and North Africa has increased, reaching about 30 percent of imports last summer.[20] By October 1973, oil arriving at U.S. ports from the Arab nations reached two million barrels per day, counting both crude oil and refined products.[21]

As U.S. crude oil production failed to keep pace with growth, oil refining capacity growth also lagged. Only two wholly new oil refineries have come on line since 1970,* while growing demand for refined products has increased the need for imported refined products. Until the Arab embargo began in 1973, U.S. refineries ran near peak capacity,** leaving almost no room for future growth in domestic product demand without a refining capacity expansion program.

Ironically, a chronic oversupply of refined products in the late 1960s was one reason why oil companies did not plan new refineries. Excess gasoline was sold by the "incremental barrel" cost concept rather than at full cost, providing a supply source for independent gasoline dealers. Low prices and vigorous sales competition prevailed. The refining industry had little incentive to expand in these circumstances.[22]

The Oil Import Program helped delay refinery construction by creating uncertainty about future crude oil availability, particularly on the East Coast where imported crude would necessarily dominate refinery feedstocks. The gradual lifting of import quotas on refined

---

* The two new refineries are Atlantic Richfield's facility at Cherry Point in Ferndale, Washington, and Mobil's at Joliet, Illinois.

** According to the American Petroleum Institute's *Weekly Statistical Bulletin,* refineries operated at an average level of 98 percent of capacity from July through November. During the first half of the year, when API measured refinery capacity slightly differently, the average operating level was 91 percent of capacity.

12

products began in 1965, when residual oil was exempted from the Import Program on the East Coast. This action encouraged petroleum companies to build refineries abroad, where cheaper labor, tax incentives and low-cost crude oil were available. Following the elimination of the Import Program last year, oil companies announced numerous new refinery expansion and construction projects in the United States.

In recent years, states and localities on the East Coast began to have doubts about the environmental desirability of refinery construction in their jurisdictions. A number of proposals to build refineries on the coastline were put forward in the late 1960s and the early 1970s, and the oil companies found themselves confronted with well-organized opposition in state and local governments and in citizen environmental organizations. Objections were raised on the basis of oil spill risks, air pollution problems, aesthetic concerns and the fear that an industrial foot in the door on the coast would bring an avalanche of secondary development, including additional refineries, petrochemical plants, supertanker ports, and power plants.*

Natural Gas

Between 1950 and 1970, natural gas provided more than half of the growth in total energy supply. Pipelines were built after World War II to transport natural gas from the Southwest producing regions to the populous Northeast and elsewhere. A growing number of homes and factories turned to natural gas because of its low cost—kept low in part by government regulation**—its clean-burning characteristics, and its general convenience. Pipelines were built to supply gas needed to meet peak demands on the coldest day of the year. Industries were attracted by low-priced "interruptible" gas contracts under which they purchased gas for delivery when there was surplus gas in the pipeline and were cut off on very cold days when the full pipeline supply was needed for residential and com-

---

* It was this last concern that led to the passage of Delaware's Coastal Zone Act in 1971. The Delaware law not only specifically prohibits oil refineries from locating in its coastal zone, but also forbids a number of other "heavy industries." Maine's Environmental Improvement Commission has also blocked a number of refinery proposals in that state, and a Rhode Island community vetoed one as well. Other jurisdictions have been more enthusiastic about the economic benefits of refineries. A Shell refinery originally planned for Delaware is now gaining the necessary permits in New Jersey.
** Prices charged for natural gas by producers at the wellhead and by transmission companies at the pipeline terminal are regulated by the Federal Power Commission. Retail distributors of natural gas are, for the most part, regulated monopolies like electric utilities. Retail gas rates are set by states through public utility commissions.

mercial customers who held "firm" contracts at higher rates.

At first the interruptions were few, making interruptible contracts a remarkable bargain. But by the early 1970s, natural gas (not pipeline capacity) was in short supply. Interruptions became common, requiring customers to shift temporarily to other fuels, primarily oil. During the last few years even some "firm" contract customers have found their natural gas cut off at times of peak demand. In some areas new gas customers have been turned away entirely. Thus, permanent shifts to oil and electricity have added to the demands for these energy sources, underscoring the inter-relatedness of energy problems.

Coal

Shortly after World War II, the railroads shifted from coal-fired steam locomotives to diesel engines, eliminating a major market for coal. At the same time, home coal furnaces were scrapped in favor of oil, gas or electricity. These factors led to a 36 percent decline in coal mine output between 1947 and 1962,[23] a blow from which the industry is only now beginning to recover.

Labor problems and poor working conditions have plagued the coal industry. Rising labor costs encouraged mining companies to turn increasingly to surface mining, which produces three times the coal output of an underground mine with the same number of man hours.[24] The persistence of mine disasters and the official recognition of "black lung" disease led to passage of the Coal Mine Health and Safety Act of 1969. Measures for safer mining resulted in slower mining; a sharp drop in underground coal mine productivity followed implementation of new safety procedures.[25] Some small mines found that mining coal safely was not profitable and had to close down. The following year Congress imposed nation-wide standards for pollutants, especially oxides of sulfur,* leading to further shifts away from coal as an industrial and electric power fuel.

Nuclear Power

Nuclear power is only beginning to be a part of our commercial energy supply. It is apparently economical, but public concerns persist as to whether it is safe. Technical problems—including equipment delivery delays, reliability problems and poor labor productivity—

---

* Standards were set by states and by the Environmental Protection Agency in accordance with the Clean Air Act of 1970.

have contributed to nuclear construction delays. The growing number of orders for nuclear power plants since the mid and late 1960s have also put a great strain on the licensing process, lengthening lead times appreciably. Procedures for public hearings and detailed technical reviews by the Atomic Energy Commission prior to construction were established years ago. The National Environmental Policy Act of 1969 extended the process to include a detailed analysis of the environmental impact of proposed plants.

The bottleneck looked particularly serious in 1971, when only one operating license was granted, but nine new plants came on line in 1972 and fifteen in 1973. Seventeen more are expected to become operable in 1974, and as many as 100 more are planned for construction in the next decade. Nuclear power provided only 5 percent of the nation's electricity at the end of 1973, but about half of the electric power capacity under construction is nuclear powered.

Why the Gap?

The roots of the current crisis lie in the gap between consumption and domestic production of energy, which began to increase in the early 1960s and continued until shortages appeared and forced emergency curtailments of energy use. Consumption grew virtually unchecked while domestic production of fuels has actually been stable since 1970. A major reason that energy consumption has grown so rapidly is that until a year ago it was a bargain compared to most other items. The price of energy, relative to the prices of other goods and services, actually declined during the 1960s. But there were other reasons on the consumption side:

(a) Rate structures for natural gas and electricity promoted more consumption by offering large-volume users a significantly lower price per Btu than small users.

(b) Promotional advertising encouraged the use of energy-consuming goods such as autos, air conditioners, home appliances, electric heating systems, color televisions, and petrochemical products (such as plastics, which require large amounts of energy in their manufacture).

(c) Construction of the interstate highway system with the billions of dollars from the Highway Trust Fund brought a rapid increase in inter-city, high-speed auto travel.

(d) Subsidies to truck and air transportation encouraged a shift in freight away from rail transport. Public expenditures for road and airport construction plus military development of aircraft later used for freight and passenger travel were among these subsidies.

(e) Passenger air fares dropped in comparison with bus and rail fares, and stimulated air traffic. While air fares increased 8 percent between 1950 and 1970, bus and rail fares increased 90 percent and 47 percent respectively.[26]

(f) Investment tax incentives and steadily rising wage rates encouraged industry to expand with energy-intensive capital equipment.

(g) The growth in suburbia, encouraged by federal income tax breaks and federally guaranteed loans for homeowners, has resulted in the soaring use of gasoline for commuting and other energy for the single-family homes that were built.

At the same time, federal government policies worked to curb growth in production of energy:

(a) The foreign tax credit, which permits oil companies to subtract the payments to host governments from their U.S. income taxes, became a greater incentive to oil production abroad—rather than at home—during the 1950s and 1960s.* Ironically, while the import quota system was trying to boost domestic oil production, the foreign tax credit was effectively stimulating oil production abroad by U.S. oil companies.

(b) FPC regulation of natural gas prices and reductions in the oil and gas depletion allowances in 1969 from 27½ percent to 22 percent were also viewed by industry and others as a deterrent to development.

(c) Price controls imposed in 1971 on fuels (as well as on other goods and services) distorted normal marketplace actions to balance supply and demand.

(d) Offshore oil and gas lease sales were virtually halted after 1969 for a year and a half.

(e) Implementation of the Coal Mine Health and Safety Act of 1969 resulted in lower productivity in underground coal mines.

(f) The National Environmental Policy Act of 1969, requiring detailed environmental impact assessments of major federal projects,

---

* Foreign payments include some income taxes but are, primarily, royalties and oil-purchasing costs which are classified as "taxes." During the 1950s and 1960s such foreign tax credits to international oil companies were enough in most cases to eliminate completely U.S. income taxes on income from oil produced abroad.

caused delays in the Trans-Alaska Pipeline, offshore lease sales, and nuclear power plants, while government agencies learned to comply adequately with its requirements.

(g) The Clean Air Act of 1970 caused industrial and power plant operators to turn away from coal to natural gas and oil to meet the sulfur oxide standards as well as automobile manufacturers to build cars with reduced fuel economy to meet emission requirements.

Most of the above policies were made because of desirable social purposes: environmental quality or economic well-being. Without them, domestic energy production might have grown at the same unchecked rate as consumption. Yet such uncontrolled production of energy would have hastened environmental degradation and might have strained our efforts to control inflation. As seen in hindsight, the trouble was not that we created economic controls and environmental laws, but that we failed to assess the impact that these policies would have on energy production and failed to develop parallel policies to curb consumption and to spur the search for new, clean sources of energy.

The growing gap has occurred because a balanced energy budget was not a high-priority item in government until very recently. Actions to conserve energy were foreign to our thinking until recent months. Other actions that increased demand or reduced supply were taken with little or no thought to their energy implications. The lesson we are now painfully learning is that balancing our energy budget is not automatic. Government policies and private actions must address energy as a high priority concern.

Section 2

Energy Policy: Objectives, Tools and Constraints

Energy Policy Objectives

Objectives for energy policy tell us where we want to go and provide a benchmark for policy successes and failures. Individuals may differ in picking out objectives, but these five would be high on most lists:
(1) Assuring reliability of energy supply;
(2) Achieving the lowest cost to society for energy;
(3) Avoiding economic and regional inequities;
(4) Safeguarding the quality of the environment; and,
(5) Minimizing international problems due to energy.

Unfortunately, in the real world these very desirable objectives are often in conflict and must be compromised. They must also be harmonized with other social goals in areas like transportation and overall fiscal and welfare policy. The scenarios described in Section 7 illustrate the wide range of outcomes which result from the tradeoffs among different objectives.

Each objective is briefly discussed below.

Assuring Reliability of Energy Supply

We have learned in recent months how much our lives and the economy can be affected by unexpected shortages of energy. By a reliable supply, we mean one that is not subject to sudden interruption and which is adequate to fuel the needs of the economy.

In assessing reliability it is important to know how vulnerable our energy sources are to sudden disruption, which can mean the loss of economic output, jobs and creature comforts. The recent unexpected shortages in energy supply have led to substantial unemployment, not only because factories lack fuel, but also because shortages have forced drastic changes in consumption patterns. The shortage of gasoline, for instance, means less trade for roadside restaurants and tourist resorts. It is possible to lessen the impact of sudden interruptions through diversifying by region and by kind of fuels. When energy comes from many sources and many places, the nation has more flexibility, not in energy policy alone but also in the other areas such as foreign policy and environmental protection.

Flexibility in use is another main ingredient in reliability of supply. The ability to burn more than one kind of fuel in a power plant, or the capability of transferring electricity from one part of the nation to another are examples of flexibility.

Achieving the Lowest Cost to Society for Energy

Consumers today are understandably concerned with soaring energy prices. Yet, prices in our economy serve important functions. They are a means of ensuring efficiency in the use of our scarce resources throughout the economy and within the energy sector itself.

Because of this function, prices should include all of the costs of production, including some which have in the past been borne by society rather than by the producing company and the consumers of the company's products. For example, the costs of avoiding air pollution emitted by a power station should be included in the price of the energy produced. On the other hand, if monopoly elements are present and prices are above a competitive level they also result in a poor allocation of resources to the detriment of consumers and the economy.

We wish to be sure that within the energy sector, either through competitive forces or through governmental action, the industry uses the most efficient technological and organizational means to deliver energy to our households, factories, offices and shops. In short, an energy industry that uses the best economically feasible technology is the one that serves best the economy and consumers.

Avoiding Economic and Regional Inequities

Sharply rising energy prices can present severe problems for poor people, who use a higher percentage of their income for their basic energy needs than do those who are better off financially.* Rising energy prices will exacerbate this imbalance. The poor will be hard-pressed to obtain the necessities of life while the more affluent need to cut but a few luxuries, since energy represents a smaller portion of their total budgets.

Energy policies alone cannot cure social inequities but they should be designed to avoid making them worse. The most important policy for avoiding poverty is to provide jobs and fair wages, and this is a major national goal. Full employment is a major objective of energy policy, and allocations to deal with the current shortage are being made with the goal of minimizing unemployment.

An efficient solution to the general problem of income distribution would be some form of direct income transfer to the poor. If this is not politically feasible, then specific energy equity policy measures ought to be considered: for example, energy stamps, like food stamps, for the poor.

Maximizing Environmental Quality

Environmental damage cannot be altogether avoided in getting and burning energy. Changing awareness of the environment, and how it may be damaged and healed, makes environmental protection a rapidly changing and difficult goal to implement. One crucial guide for energy policy stands out, however. Energy policy must be acutely sensitive to energy activities that may irreparably damage the environment for decades or even generations to come.

Attention to the environment also requires bringing environmental considerations into the energy planning process long before new technologies or new energy installations are in place. Technologies should be built with environmental quality as a constraint, rather than as an afterthought.

Minimizing International Problems Due to Energy

Another objective of energy policy is to leave the United States as flexible as possible in carrying out its relations with other countries. Energy policy should be seen as only one part of the foreign policy of the nation. This objective is discussed separately in Section 3.

---

* See page 3 for definition of income groups.

Policy Directions

In our economy, both public and private institutions make policy. In times of crisis, attention tends to be concentrated on the role of government. The extent to which economic life continues without direct government intervention, even in the energy sector which is subject to more government intervention than most, is usually underestimated. The market system—that is, the interaction of demand, supply and prices—is still of major importance in determining what is produced and consumed in our economy. The success of government policies depends to a large extent on how effectively they work in harmony with the market system to serve policy objectives.

When people speak of a national energy policy, they usually mean some plan of government action. But any policy is likely to rely on a combination of both private and government initiative including state and local governments and regulatory bodies, as well as the federal government. Very few people nowadays would support the extreme views that the government should do everything, or that everything should be left to the market system. The debate centers more usually on what roles should be assigned to the public and private sectors in carrying out policy.

The following brief examination of some of the strengths and weaknesses of both the market system and governmental intervention provides some background to this debate.

Reliance on the Market: Prices as Signals

The amount of energy used and produced is the result of a large number of apparently unrelated decisions by just about every American. A factor entering into all of these decisions is how much energy costs. People will tend to use more energy when it is cheaper, less when it is expensive. Conversely, those who produce energy will normally have greater incentive to produce more at higher prices than at lower prices. Changing prices provide signals to both producers and consumers of energy. The reaction to these signals may vary in speed and extent, but so long as they exist at all, they provide a basis for automatic market adjustment and permit the individual consumer or producer some freedom of choice in the process.

On occasions this adjustment process may be too slow or in other ways inadequate to serve policy aims. Today energy supply and demand are not sufficiently responsive to price changes to avoid severe short run problems. On the demand side, consumers may not have accurate information available to help them in decisionmaking. Furthermore, they are stuck with their large automobiles and glass houses, even though the prices of fuel and gasoline have jumped up. For those reasons, and because energy is a relatively small yet essential part of household and many industry costs, the demand for energy may be relatively insensitive to price changes in the short run. Over the longer term, when equipment and energy-consuming habits can be changed, demand is more responsive.

On the supply side too, the response to price changes may be too slow. The long lead times necessary to the development of some sorts of energy supplies reduce the flexibility of response in unforeseen contingencies.

If competition is absent, rising prices do not always lead to increased production. One third of all oil supplies comes from members of the Organization of the Petroleum Exporting Countries (OPEC) whose monopoly position has permitted them to increase prices sharply, yet still control production levels. And as long as some basic fuels are scarce on the domestic market, higher prices may lead to higher profits rather than increased production.

Just as demand does, supply becomes more responsive to price changes over the long run. Even a sharp rise in prices may not be sufficient to draw out significantly increased production of existing fuels in the short run; but, over time, high prices encourage the development of new sources, thus adding to total supplies.

The lag time in responding to price signals requires the kind of emergency actions to allocate the shortage which are now under way. But that is not a reason for continuing governmental involvement in energy. There is a more fundamental reason for governmental intervention: price signals are incomplete. They fail to reflect many of the energy problems that concern society.

Environmental protection, for example, is not effectively enforced by market prices under existing rules. The reason is that much of the nation's air and water are still considered free, and the pollutants of energy production are dumped into them without charge. Similarly, gasoline prices do not reflect the inconvenience and cost borne by those who suffer property damage from oil spills. Charging the energy producers with these costs could be an important incentive to encourage pollution control, as a supplement to direct control by regulation.

Energy supplies that are reliable are certainly worth more than supplies subject to sudden interruption as has recently occurred with respect to Middle East oil. Yet the market price alone does not reflect a difference, for example, in the price of oil from Texas as contrasted with oil from Saudi Arabia. In fact, until recently Saudi Arabian oil could be purchased in the United States at lower prices than domestic oil; one reason given in the past to justify government intervention in the form of import quotas was to limit the incursion of potentially unstable supplies.

Sometimes benefits, as well as costs, are not reflected in the price of energy. For example, the fruits of research and development (R&D) of new energy systems largely flow to society rather than to the private firms undertaking the research because often they do not involve patentable inventions. Even if they are patentable, the major benefits may be in controlling pollution or reducing energy costs; these benefits cannot be captured by the company that perfects the new technology. This means that most private firms are reluctant to undertake this type of research and there is underinvestment in R&D unless the government assumes an active role in the financing.

A competitive industry is of course a prerequisite for a market-oriented solution to pricing. Consumer protection against monopoly profits is a traditional role for governmental intervention in the market place. In the energy field, the electric power and gas utilities are natural monopolies that have always been subject to price controls. A national debate is in full swing as to whether competitive forces are adequate in the fuels industry.[1]

Government Intervention:
The Use of Policy Tools

The economically justified purpose for governmental intervention is to correct inadequate competitive forces and to satisfy public concerns not reflected in market prices. But often in the past government intervention has simply been a response to the power of special interest groups.

Whether the basis for governmental intervention is economic or political, the tools of intervention are pretty much the same: taxes and subsidies, research and development, regulation, and governmental ownership.

Before examining the corrective tools which the government has at its disposal for making changes in energy matters, it must be emphasized that just about everything the government does has some impact on the energy sector. In the past, for example, growth in energy consumption has been very closely associated with growth in the economy. As we have seen, fiscal and monetary policies designed to stimulate or restrain the economy or consumer expenditures can have major effects on the amount of energy produced and consumed. Environmental laws and foreign policies also greatly affect energy supply and demand.

At present, of course, the energy scene is dominated by a package of measures designed to deal with emergency dislocations in supplies. These include moral suasion, price controls and various forms of rationing. While they may take the nation out of the present energy crunch they are a completely inadequate set of tools for developing policies for the future in a way that will satisfy our multiple policy objectives. The government has more effective policy tools it can call upon to correct the inadequacies of the market place with respect to the energy field.

Taxes and Subsidies

The basic function of taxes is to raise revenues. However, in the energy field, tax policies have also been used for decades as a means of encouraging exploration and development—primarily for oil and gas. These policies include: (1) the depletion allowance, which allows producers to deduct from taxable income a percentage share of the income from production each year—22 percent in the case of gas and oil. It permits total deductions many times greater than the actual investment costs over the lifetime of the property; (2) the expensing of intangible costs, under which all development or drilling costs (except for those items which have salvage value) can be written off as current expenses, thus decreasing the current income subject to taxes; (3) the tax credits for payments to foreign governments which offset all payments to foreign governments against American corporate income tax liabilities. One effect of all these tax benefits, which are in effect subsidies to producers, has been to make prices lower than they otherwise would have been for oil.

By increasing retail prices of energy, taxes can be used to curtail demand. Taxes can be used to help clean up the environment by charging polluters for discharging wastes into the air and water. Such taxes would also help balance our energy budget by folding into prices more of the real costs of energy production, thus discouraging wasteful consumption while encouraging suppliers to reduce their pollutants. Excess profits taxes can be used to tax away windfall profits which are determined to be in excess of the level of profits needed to induce additional supplies. The problem is that excess profits taxes are extremely cumbersome to administer and can lead to extravagant and wasteful practices by corporations in order to avoid payment of the taxes. Taxes on imports or exports can also be used to regulate trade in energy.

Governmental investments and subsidies are a most powerful instrument of energy policy. Governmental dollars and guarantees can be used to encourage mass transit, bicycle paths, loans to insulate homes, and all sorts of activities that might save energy or enlarge supply in the future. Subsidies can be indirect, as in the case of the tax treatment of oil and gas production noted above. Or they can be direct, as in the case of R&D, discussed below.

Research and Development

Funds for research leading to development of new energy sources and technologies to conserve energy provide another powerful tool for government policy makers. Energy R&D spending is being increased in a substantial way. We look to new technology for a large part of the solution to future energy problems, but there is little immediate effect from current efforts, because lead times for energy R&D are very long. Results will be felt, not next month or next year, but in 1985 or 2001 AD and beyond. Yet it is essential to invest now in the energy future of the twenty-first century.[2]

Governmental Regulation

This category includes all of the government-imposed standards ranging from licensing, emission standards, state and local utility regulation, regulation of natural gas prices, anti-trust legislation, import and export quotas, etc. The rationale behind regulation as a policy is usually the inadequacy of a market approach.

When regulation is used by government to implement policy, it is usually characterized by the establishment of an administrative agency with a specific mandate guided by legislative standards. Examples are the Environmental Protection Agency, which enforces the

25

standards of the Clean Air and Clean Water Acts, and the Atomic Energy Commission which regulates safety in nuclear plants.

Regulation is a plausible solution where there is a public demand for standards to achieve a clear purpose like environmental protection or price controls. The major shortcoming of regulation is that it rarely performs as well as its proponents expect. Mandates may be ignored for lack of funding. Agencies may be captured by the very groups they are meant to regulate—not necessarily through villainy, but more likely through the gradual development of common interests, a harmonious view of problems, and an interchange of manpower between the regulator and the regulated. Regulatory agencies may also be extremely susceptible to rigidity in substantive and procedural issues, making their responses painfully slow.

Despite these limitations, regulation is sometimes the best way to achieve a desired result, particularly if the market appears incapable of meeting social objectives. Public and legislative vigilance would undoubtedly enable the agencies to better their performance in the carrying out of their mandates.

Public Ownership and Resource Development

Public ownership is a policy tool that has been used sparingly in the United States. Government-owned companies have been established in the electric power industry, and the government is at present the sole proprietor of uranium enrichment plants. In both instances the federal energy role was a by-product of long-accepted federal functions: flood control and regional development for TVA and national defense for atomic energy. Even so, more direct federal action is an option often suggested for development of oil and gas resources on the federal domain, and for other purposes. The extent of public ownership is an important consideration whenever this tool is discussed. Limiting public ownership to a "yardstick" or example-setting function to spur more effective performance in the private sector stops short of subjecting the entire industry to nationalization.

The energy field is characterized by another aspect of public ownership. With the Department of the Interior acting as custodian, the American people own the bulk of the remaining fossil fuel resources in the United States. This subject is discussed in Section 5. It is relevant here in the sense that government ownership of the fuels might be a justification for the government to engage directly in their development.

Institutional Issues

To better understand how energy policy has been made in the past, and to provide a means of exploring needed reforms, the Project has commissioned studies of government decisionmaking for energy policy.[3] These studies are designed to raise issues in areas where reform may be in order.

First, adequate information is fundamental to making policy effectively. Data on short term energy supplies, on reserves, and on the impacts of energy development are at present incomplete and fragmented. Decisions are made in a cloud of uncertainty. To dispel the cloud, it might be useful to establish a centralized governmental energy data bank; to require industry to submit essential information for use in the data bank; and to accelerate government research and analysis, and make it available to the public in understandable form.

Another problem is that responsibility for government energy policy planning has long been fragmented into many different agencies which tend to deal with emergencies as they arise; but they are ill-equipped to formulate long term strategies which consider the impacts of alternative courses of action.

Further, some areas of national energy planning are inaccessible to citizens. The National Environmental Policy Act, which requires federal agencies to prepare impact statements for major actions, does provide a chance for citizens to be heard. Regional planning organizations could add to these opportunities, particularly for people who live in areas especially affected by energy development. Industry might be required to disclose development proposals, so that citizens and local governments could take a hand in the planning in a timely way.

Deciding which level of government is responsible for a particular energy decision is an important issue. States, through their traditional regulations of land use, energy facility siting, and resource development, play a vital role. But at times individual state actions may not be consonant with national objectives.

New governmental organizations might help to focus public sentiment on energy, to use a new information base for improved planning, and to coordinate the various federal and state agencies with energy responsibility. In recognition of these needs the Federal Energy Office was recently created; however it has been preoccupied primarily with short term issues. Congress is considering creating in the Executive Branch an Energy Policy Council and a cabinet level energy department, which would address many of the problems of policy development and implementation.

It must be realized, however, that government reorganization is not a panacea. Making the tradeoffs discussed in the next section will be difficult; each competing point of view will be strongly advocated and debated. Better institutions may help to make the debate more productive.

Energy Policy: Tradeoffs and Values

We have identified objectives for an energy policy but we know that they often conflict with each other. Certain ways to secure an adequate supply will conflict with a clean environment. Any policy ultimately involves making choices which "trade off" objectives against each other. To the extent possible, these decisions should be made on the best assessment of benefits and costs. Yet no matter how thorough the factual information, there will always remain some areas dependent on society's values rather than on more facts. To the extent that such value areas are clearly defined, and it is recognized that their resolution is properly a matter for the political arena, we have sharpened the energy policy dialogue.

The major purpose of policy analysis is to organize knowledge in such a way as to help the nation make choices. To our minds the most fundamental choice is a sense of direction about growth in energy consumption. For that reason the basic analysis of the Project is presented in the form of the three alternative futures outlined in Section 7. A more detailed discussion of these alternatives and the strengths and weakness of each from an energy policy perspective will constitute the essence of our final report.

The essential work of the Project—working out the long term implications of different patterns of energy growth—has accustomed us to think in decades and quarter centuries. Recent world events have telescoped and brought closer the long term issues. Accordingly, we have attempted to use our research to explore the choices that are open to the nation in the next two or three years in the face of energy shortages, with an eye on the long lasting, possibly irreversible effects of those choices. This is the subject of Section 6.

In order to make an overall assessment of near-term choices, it is important to understand three issues that are especially pressing. There may be no escaping some immediate decisions on foreign policy, the environment, and federal government management of the resources the people own, all of which bear in essential ways on energy policy. The next three sections outline some of the complexities of these subjects, in an effort to clarify the consequences, both early and late, of energy decisions.

SECTION 3

U.S. Energy Policy in the World Arena

THE PROJECT HAS concentrated its analysis on U.S. energy policy, but obviously the United States is an integral part of a world-wide system of energy supply and demand. A major inquiry into the international implications of energy, which the Project commissioned from the Brookings Institution, is in progress.[1] This section, which reflects the tentative thinking of the Project's staff, attempts to provide the reader a frame of reference for relating U.S. energy policy to an interdependent world.

Several features appear to dominate the international energy scene: the cartel of oil exporting countries; the political volatility of the Middle East; the creaky world monetary system; the ominous repercussions of the energy crisis upon poor countries; and the global nature of certain environmental problems.

The Cartel

The sparsely populated lands around the Persian Gulf contain well over half of the world's proven oil reserves. (See Figure 4 and Appendix C, Table 6.) In 1973, the oil-rich nations of that region asked for and got a four-fold increase in crude oil prices. "The era of cheap oil for the industrialized world is finished," said the Shah of Iran, in one of the year's more memorable understatements.

In times past, a handful of American and European petroleum companies with far-flung international operations dominated the world oil market. Now, however, a cartel of major oil-exporting countries—led by the Persian Gulf states—is doing the dominating.

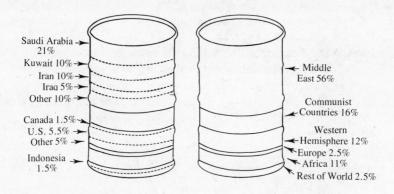

Figure 4. World Petroleum Reserves, 1973

Historically, cartels—made up of suppliers of a given commodity (such as cotton)—have never lasted very long. Either one or more of the parties broke away to make lower-priced deals with buyers in order to secure a larger share of the market, or new suppliers, attracted by high prices, entered the market and undercut the cartel's monopoly power. How long will the oil-producing countries continue to act in concert? No one really knows, of course, although there seem to be good reasons for caution in predicting an early collapse.

For one thing, no significant new suppliers of oil—another Saudi Arabia or Kuwait—are visible on the horizon. Meanwhile, the West Europeans continue to be dependent upon the Middle East for 70 percent of their oil, and the Japanese get about 40 percent of their oil from that region. In addition, Middle Eastern leaders state that it makes good economic sense to them to prolong the life of their non-renewable resources by slowing their production increases. As they watch their foreign reserves pile up in New York, London and Zurich, and as they begin to draw up plans for their own industrialization, which will someday require oil, their monopoly practice looks to them like enlightened self-interest. The actual *cost* of producing Middle Eastern oil is still very low, less than 20 cents per barrel; the huge disparity between cost and price may eventually lead to some erosion of the cartel. But it also gives these producing nations a wide margin of maneuverability. If, for example, new sources such as oil shale become competitive, the Middle Eastern producers can simply cut their prices, say, from $8 per barrel to $6 and still profit handsomely.

The United States is less dependent on Arab oil than is West

Europe or Japan. About 15 percent of the nation's total energy supply is imported; about 35 percent of U.S. oil is imported, mainly from Canada and Venezuela. Before the 1973 embargo, more than 10 percent of the oil consumed in the United States came from Arab nations. As we have seen in Section 1, however, even these figures are deceptive. As U.S. domestic oil production leveled off in recent years, the nation increasingly depended on the Middle Eastern barrel of oil to fill new demand.

Conflict in the Middle East

Consider the following: four wars in four decades; mile upon mile of bitterly contested frontiers; hundreds of thousands of refugees; deep bitterness and mistrust; no resolution in sight. The continuing volatility of the Middle East remains an ever important fact of life in energy considerations, especially for the United States.

For example, an energy policy which assumes that Arab oil will meet most U.S. growth in the years ahead would be at odds with a foreign policy which supported the negotiating position of Israel. Getting more energy is not the only U.S. purpose in the Middle East. Israel's continuing survival as a nation-state and avoidance of a U.S.-U.S.S.R. confrontation, which could endanger the whole world's peace, are obviously concerns for Americans, as public opinion polls over the years have amply demonstrated. In as troubled an area as the Middle East, if foreign and energy policy aims do not at least complement each other, the United States runs the risk of one or the other failing.

It is important to note that the political problems associated with importing oil differ markedly, depending upon the country or region from where the oil originates. The threat of a nation cutting off oil to the United States in order to gain political leverage is much more remote, for instance, when the oil is coming from western Canada rather than the Persian Gulf. Even within the Persian Gulf region, political distinctions must be made between, for instance, non-Arab Iran and Arab Kuwait.

The same cannot be said about oil imports and economics. Very few distinctions need be made, it seems, when it comes to money. During the recent crisis, while the Arab nations proclaimed an embargo of the United States and the Netherlands, all oil exporting nations raised prices significantly including Canada, Venezuela, and

Iran. Importing oil from any nation, whatever its politics, poses an inescapable problem today—how to pay the high prices.

The World Monetary System

Soaring prices for so essential a commodity as oil have strained an already creaky world monetary system.

Since the end of the 1960s, periodic international monetary crises have occurred. One by one, the major trading nations of the world have abandoned the fixed exchange rates of the system in effect since World War II, and have floated their currencies. While the new system has worked out better than many anticipated, it is vulnerable to the sudden dislocation threatened by increased oil prices.

At present consumption levels, oil revenues to producing countries are expected to rise fourfold from $27 billion last year to $95 billion in this. Some nations, such as Iran or Venezuela, may be able to absorb much of their increased revenues in development projects at home, but most other producing nations will not. The largest portion of the $95 billion will be seeking investment opportunities where they are most readily available—in the rich, oil-consuming nations.

Over the longer run, adjustments are likely to be made in the system to accommodate the oil producers' new revenues. There is an acute need for capital investment funds throughout the world and the oil producers are under pressure to find investment opportunities in order to keep abreast of inflation. But in the short term, the sharp changes in international monetary flows are causing serious financial uncertainty.

Increased oil producer revenues, of course, mean high bills for consuming countries. These extra payments will be made by the importing countries through drawing down reserves, by reducing imports of oil or other goods, or by increasing exports in order to generate higher exchange earnings to pay for the oil. But the pressure to increase export earnings and reduce imports could lead to intense competition in export markets, and possibly towards import restrictions by some. Given the increasing interdependence of countries— foreign trade is rising much more rapidly than the growth in the world economy—the erection of trade barriers could undercut export industries, resulting in a consequent decline in economic output and a rise of unemployment.

Impact on Poor Countries

The more than 400 percent increase in oil prices dealt the poor countries where the majority of mankind lives, a far more savage economic blow than it did America, Europe, or Japan.

For the poor countries, before the crisis in oil prices, came the crises in food prices in the summer and autumn of 1973.[2] Wheat went from less than $2 per bushel to more than $5; rough rice, which in 1972 sold for 5 to 8 cents per pound, sold for 12 to 20 cents; soybeans rose from $3 per bushel to more than $6 per bushel, hitting a peak of more than $10 per bushel.

The drought-stricken countries of Africa and South Asia were hard pressed to find money for essential food imports. Added to that, the increases in oil prices have placed many African and South Asian countries without their own oil resources in the most dire economic straits in decades.

Latin American countries are less hard hit. Mexico and Argentina are practically self-sufficient in oil. Many Latin American countries—Venezuela, Ecuador, Colombia—are oil exporters. Brazil is the region's largest oil importer, but the Brazilian government appears confident that it can pay for its oil with rapidly expanding exports and world-wide price increases for many of its commodities—such as soybeans, which it exports. The plight of the small oil-importing countries of Latin America is comparable to that of the oil-importing countries of Asia and Africa. They do not know where the foreign exchange to pay for food, fuel and fertilizers will come from.

India has already announced a 15 percent reduction in oil imports, which may seriously affect that nation's oil-based fertilizer industry. Industrial production is threatened too. In order to begin her latest Five Year Plan for economic growth at 5½ percent a year, India would have to pay $1¼ billion to cover her crude oil import needs during 1974. This is about 40 percent of her potential export earnings for the year, and twice her foreign exchange reserves. It is an impossible drain. India will be fortunate to manage half this level of oil imports at present prices.[3]

Not many poor countries have plans as ambitious as India's for industrial development, but are devoting their efforts to improved agriculture. The Green Revolution, which is dependent on cheap chemical fertilizers and has contributed significantly to growth in agriculture production in Asia, is seriously imperiled by high fuel and fertilizer prices. This points to decreased food production in many poor countries on top of the high food prices. For the short term, the lives of millions depend on explicit and rapid policy actions to provide aid in one form or another from the oil-exporting nations and the rich industrialized nations, as well as from the international organizations which they support.

Global Environmental Problems

Many energy-associated environmental problems are global in nature and must be solved in concert with other nations or not at all.

The safeguarding of nuclear material is an excellent example, according to one of the Project's studies.[4] The theft of nuclear weapon materials from one nation's civilian nuclear power program by a terrorist or criminal group poses a threat to every nation on earth. Another instance is oil pollution of the oceans. Project studies indicate[5] that concerted action by the United States and other major oil-consuming nations is required to prevent oil spills.

U.S. Policy Options

These comments are meant to be suggestive. The Project will analyze in detail the full range of the United States' international options in energy policy in its final report.

Of course, the United States cannot unilaterally solve the world oil problem. And U.S. energy policy is as likely to be shaped by world events as the opposite.

Most of the basic U.S. options seem to lie somewhere between two extremes—importing a larger portion of U.S. energy growth *or* rapid development of U.S. energy sources—perhaps not only for the capability of self-sufficiency, but in time to become a net energy exporter. But no energy-related policies fit neatly between these poles. Questions concerning the level of assistance for poor countries are independent of these options. And some issues, such as energy conservation, cut across all the options. The less energy the United States consumes, the less will be the international problems associated with almost any energy policy option.

Growing Middle Eastern Imports

A return to the situation before the 1973 Arab-Israeli war—that is, of rapidly growing U.S. oil imports from the Middle East—would put this country in direct competition with the other oil-importing nations of the world, friend and foe, rich and poor alike, for any increased production by the major exporters. This option raises serious questions, not the least of which are: Will the Middle Eastern nations increase their growth in production? What will be the political price? What would be the impact on U.S. balance of payments, and on the economies of Europe, Japan, The Third World; and, how would U.S. relations with them be affected?

In addition, growing imports would require significant stockpiles of oil, either in the form of stored oil or developed but non-producing wells, as insurance against interruptions. As the upcoming discussion of stockpiling in Section 6 reveals, this is a very costly business. The only thing more costly would be not doing it.

Self-Sufficiency

A program of energy self-sufficiency, such as "Project Independence" announced by President Nixon in late 1973, raises a whole different set of questions. Can the United States develop its resources at a greatly accelerated pace without doing irrevocable damage to the nation's health and environment? (See Section 4.) Will the United States' going it alone in energy encourage Japan and West European nations to make bilateral agreements with the producing nations? How would this affect non-rich nations?

Moreover, even with domestic self-sufficiency, there is no escaping the fact that Middle Eastern oil is still very low *cost*. At current prices domestic oil shale and synthetic oil from coal may look economical, but there is no guarantee that in an open market the Middle East producers would not undersell them in years to come. Will higher-cost domestic energy sources require artificial protection —in the form of quotas, tariffs or industry subsidies? How would such protectionism affect general U.S. policy of encouraging free trade with other nations, especially for its exports? Will domestic consumers have to pay higher-than-necessary prices for this energy? Of course, the cause of U.S. self-sufficiency could also be advanced by reducing our energy consumption growth rate (see Section 7) as well as by more rapid development of domestic fuels.

Perhaps, in the long run, the international problems of U.S. self-sufficiency could be ameliorated by taking domestic production a step further and supplying other energy-importing nations as well as ourselves. A first step could involve major increases in coal exports so that those nations not able to buy the oil they need could substitute American coal. (The inherent social and technical problems of increasing coal production are addressed in Section 6.)

Over the longer term, U.S. oil from shale and coal could conceivably provide a ceiling for world oil prices. This approach, buttressed by the appropriate agreements with importing countries, offers an interesting alternative to a possible consumer cartel or uncontrolled competition for world oil. But the price in terms of environmental degradation might be high.

In this context it is important to recall that oil is the most important energy source from an international viewpoint, but it is not the only one. The United States presently imports growing volumes of natural gas and exports moderate amounts of coal, plus uranium enrichment services and energy-producing and -converting equipment in significant measure.

Conclusion

The world-wide nature of energy has now intruded upon our daily lives. Whatever courses of action the United States ultimately takes to deal with energy-related problems, the ramifications of world energy realities—the producers' cartel, the Arab-Israeli conflict, the monetary system, the global environment—must be taken into account if they are to be realistic. The problems will not be solved in isolation or by groups of nations confronting each other. Accommodations must be reached that protect the legitimate interests of buyers and sellers, rich and poor. This will require international discussions in which all can participate.

The most immediate and real problems for most people in this world are the shortages of fuel, fertilizers and food in Africa, South Asia and parts of Latin America. Imaginative and generous forms of multilateral assistance to these peoples from the industrialized nations and oil exporters is needed.

SECTION 4

Environment and Energy

IN COUNTLESS WAYS energy enhances the quality of our lives. But energy pollutes. Wherever energy is produced or used there will be some disruption of the natural world which can adversely affect human health and welfare.

The Energy Policy Project has commissioned several major outside studies on significant environmental issues, and the EPP staff is in the midst of developing a framework for analyzing energy/environmental issues. While our research is not yet completed, we describe here our preliminary thoughts about environmental issues. We hope that our analysis may be useful in making sure that proper consideration of environmental impacts, especially long term impacts, is not lost in the heat of the present crisis. Of the problems we discuss in the following pages, it is our tentative judgment that three issues stand out as most significant for the period from now until the year 2000:

- air pollution, where the damage is continuous and some costs are crudely measurable;
- nuclear power uncertainties, where the likelihood of serious accidents may be small but the possible damage is great;
- land use problems, especially the commitment of hitherto undeveloped regions to intensive energy-related activities.

Before turning to specific environmental problems, let us first briefly consider the general relationship between energy use and environmental quality.

General Environmental Aspects of Energy Use

It is important to understand how the level of energy use relates to environmental quality. Given a certain state of the art in control technology, pollution increases with energy use. But it is often argued that reduction of energy use is incompatible with a clean environment, since it takes energy to clean up pollution. To better understand this issue, we commissioned a University of Michigan study[1] on the energy needed to control pollution. Results indicate that the extra energy needed to meet environmental goals is modest, about 3 percent of total use. Slower growth in energy use would not preclude having enough energy for pollution control.

Second, the less energy needed, the greater the flexibility in choosing among supply options. This nation has coal enough to last for centuries; oil and gas for at least the rest of the century; nuclear fuels for several decades if used in present-day reactors, and for centuries if used in "breeder" reactors. Vast quantities of oil are trapped in shale; and geothermal resources can meet some energy needs, particularly in the West.

Even so, our preliminary analysis tells us that all supply options must be pursued vigorously and simultaneously if historical rates of demand continue. But if demand growth slows substantially, we can forego the options that are most objectionable. These points are elaborated in the scenarios discussion in Section 7.

Third, reduced energy growth buys time for the development of better pollution control technologies. For example, from 1975 to 1985, sulfur dioxide (SO_2) controls on coal-fired power plants will be limited by the rate at which equipment can be made and installed. It is hard enough to install these devices in existing plants. Equiping new plants adds to the strain. The demand for control equipment would be easier to meet if the growth in coal-fired power plants is slower.

Air Pollution

Air pollution effects are difficult to quantify. However, a 1973 report[2] issued by the U.S. Environmental Protection Agency estimated the costs of air pollution at $16.1 billion for 1968:

- $5.2 billion for residential property damage;
- $4.7 billion for damage to inert materials;
- $0.1 billion for vegetation damage;
- $6.1 billion for damage to human health.

It must be understood that these figures are not hard and fast; value judgments are involved. But the estimate is useful in pointing out the tremendous costs associated with air pollution damage. A more recent EPA report[3] indicates that since 1968 these damage costs have dropped, owing both to increased use of air pollution controls and to the switch by power plants from coal to fuel oil and natural gas. If we postpone implementing air quality goals because of energy shortages and go back to greater use of coal, then the 1968 estimates may not be out of line.

There are strong pressures to delay putting air quality goals into full effect. A basic issue is the control of sulfur dioxide emissions. Recently, the Department of Health, Education, and Welfare reevaluated the health effects of SO_2 to determine whether the air quality standards should be loosened. The study[4] found that SO_2 concentration levels of twice the current standards clearly produce adverse health effects and that there may be adverse effects at about the level of the current standards. The report concluded that there is no human health basis for relaxing the standards.

Another recent report[5] released by the Environmental Protection Agency assessed air quality standards generally in terms of safety margins. The report states that there is no clear margin of safety for any pollutant above the legal standard. There is little or no safety margin at all for SO_2 or particles.

Economic arguments cannot always justify environmental controls, because of the difficulty of quantifying damages. But they do make a convincing case for control of sulfur oxides. The EPA estimated[2] that about $8 billion of the 1968 air pollution damages could be attributed to SO_2, roughly half of it ($4 billion) due to SO_2 emissions from power plants. Our preliminary estimates suggest that the cost of controlling this pollutant is probably not greater than the cost of the damage from the pollution. Putting sulfur oxide controls on the power plants that caused $4 billion in damages in 1968 would not, for example, cost more than $3 billion per year, including fixed charges and operating costs.

The air pollution issue is critical today because many proposed solutions to the present crisis could hurt air quality. We are switching some oil-fired power plants back to coal. Within a year it is possible to replace up to 600,000 barrels/day of fuel oil with 60 million tons/year of coal.[6] Without proper pollution controls, this could involve serious damage to human health. Preliminary results of an EPP study by the American Public Health Association[7] help us estimate the results of such a switch to higher sulfur fuels without controls. If the SO_2 pollution occurred in densely populated places, it could cause in one year an extra 13 to 14 thousand cases of respiratory disease in children under five, and about 12 thousand additional deaths of people over sixty. Many more people would be afflicted with illness and discomfort that are not easily quantified.

In the light of these tentative findings, other options, such as curbing demand, should be carefully considered. For example, reducing transportation energy use by 7 percent would save about the same amount of oil as would the power plant switch to coal. This could be done with measures such as gasoline rationing and airline rescheduling (see Sections 6–7). By-products of this option would be better air quality and less traffic congestion. The tradeoff here is between transportation inconvenience and damage to human health, even loss of lives.

The Project finds a significant, but seldom discussed, unsolved air pollution problem is that of airborne small particles from burning fossil fuels. Current technology makes it possible to remove from smoke stacks the particles that are larger than about one micron in diameter. These are visible as smoke. But it is not possible to remove small particles, which are visible as haze, or to control emissions that contribute to small particle formation.[8] There is growing evidence that these smaller particles, which can lodge in the deep recesses of the lung, are the ones most responsible for adverse health effects. Small particles can interact with sulfur dioxide (SO_2) in the air to create a much worse health hazard than can SO_2 or particle pollution independently. For example, metallic particles in the air help to convert SO_2 into sulfuric acid and sulfates—pollutants more hazardous than SO_2 itself.[4] At present there are no standards for sulfate air pollution.

There is growing evidence that small particles tend to worsen the impact of other pollutants. Another example of this is that harmful trace elements that are released in burning fossil fuels are found in the highest concentration with these small particles.[9] Small particles may carry these elements into the lungs; from there they may enter the bloodstream and interfere with body functions. Both oil and coal bear trace elements. As will be seen below, the trace element hazard varies from one type of coal to another.

The problem of large particle pollution is worse for coal than for oil. But the small particle problem may be about as bad for both,[10] so that switching from coal to oil would not help.

This problem may prove to be the most significant environmental constraint limiting expansion of fossil fuel use in the next twenty years. It must be solved if we are to achieve a clean and healthful environment. Standards must be formulated, and research on their health impacts continued. Technology to reduce small particle levels in the air should be given top research and development priority.[11]

Another important problem is the reduction of automotive air pollution. Federal standards limit evaporative fuel loss and the exhaust emissions of nitrogen oxides, hydrocarbons, and carbon monoxide. In order to comply with more stringent standards, U.S. auto manufacturers have decided to install catalytic converters in most 1975 models. Besides reducing these pollutants, the converters have the advantage over present devices of allowing the engine to be "returned" to a more efficient condition. In fact, this system is expected to regain most, if not all, of the loss in fuel economy due to earlier pollution controls.[12]

Unfortunately, the catalytic converter introduces an additional problem of uncertain magnitude. It is now known that automobiles equipped with this device emit sulfate particles through reactions in the catalytic converter with sulfur in the fuel.[4] Although the total amount of sulfate emitted would be small, these emissions could be significant because they would occur where people are, especially in urban areas. The best available estimates suggest that measurable adverse health effects could occur as early as two or three years after the introduction of the catalytic converters. This question is receiving further study.

As new controls appear on the scene and as knowledge of environmental impacts improves, air pollution problems will change. One that is likely to receive increasing attention is that of nitrogen oxide emissions. Few health studies are available today on the effects of nitrogen oxides. The air quality standard set for nitrogen dioxide is subject to considerable controversy.[13] The EPA has taken the position that the nitrogen oxide auto emissions standard set for 1977 is not needed to protect human health and has asked that Congress relax this emission standard by five times its present level, until 1982. But concern remains that exposures to nitrous acid, nitric acid, and suspended particulate intrates have not been adequately considered.[5]

The history of our experience with air pollution problems suggests that we are not likely to find them less serious as we learn more about their effects. It is more probable that as one problem is "solved" another will be identified. Air pollution is not a transient concern.

Land Use

The land use issue covers a multitude of vexing problems. It includes strip mining for coal, power plant siting, building refineries next to beaches. More significant than the sheer quantities of land involved are the multiplying effects of changing land use patterns from energy activities. Energy growth may mean opening "unspoiled" areas to energy/industrial operations. Two cases stand out. First, if domestic oil and gas is to increase significantly, there will be development of the Atlantic, Pacific and Alaskan offshore resources. Onshore support operations—terminals, refineries, petrochemical plants—will follow. In many places, this would mean trading natural beaches or marshes for industrial development.

In the Rocky Mountain region, the exploitation of coal and oil shale would lead to an influx of population and industry. Today the region is sparsely populated, primarily agrarian, devoted to ranching and to preserving environmental values. If minemouth power plants were built to burn coal, or if synthetic fuels from coal were produced in plants near the coal mines, the effects in the locality of development would be especially severe. An alternative would be to shift the development to already industrialized areas by exporting the coal for processing there. The tradeoffs here are between spoiling parts of the relatively undeveloped Rocky Mountain region with development and increasing pollution where more people live.

Another important problem is the siting question. It is increasingly difficult to find sites for energy facilities, such as refineries and power plants. New facilities are usually very large and serve a broad region; few people welcome them in their backyard. The greater the growth in energy, the sharper will be the conflicts among local, regional and national interests.

So far we have considered general environmental impacts of energy systems. But there are also special problems with particular fuels.

Coal

Coal presents many environmental problems that will hinder its rapid growth, at least in the near future. First, underground mining in the East has long been the most hazardous industrial occupation in the United States. Recently, under the Coal Mining Health and Safety Act of 1969, conditions have begun to improve, but the safety record is still poor. There is no reason that underground coal mining health and safety conditions cannot improve further. In Europe, especially in Great Britain, mining has for decades been much safer than mining in this country. Moreover, advanced mining techniques are potentially able to reduce the number of workers needed in mines.[14] Such technology should be vigorously pursued. There is much more coal ultimately available by deep mining than by stripping, about twelve times as much. Surface mining which denudes large areas, creates soil erosion, pollutes surface waters, destroys wildlife habitats and degrades land values, poses many problems that are difficult to solve. Because of this, given increased mechanization and stronger enforcement of safety measures, there is a future for U.S. underground mining.

Reclamation problems for coal surface mining are qualitatively different in each of three regions: Appalachia, the Midwest, and the West.

Much of the surface mining in Appalachia is in hilly terrain where reclamation is difficult, if not impossible. A total ban against strip mining on slopes steeper than 20 degrees is widely recommended. Such a ban would likely have a significant short-term impact, as about 15 percent of total U.S. coal production[15] is surface mined on such steep slopes in Appalachia; about half of this production is low-sulfur coal (less than 1 percent sulfur).[16] Utilities denied this low-sulfur coal would have a short-term problem of finding replacement fuel if this production were stopped abruptly. For the longer term, a ban on surface mining on slopes above 20 degrees would have little impact. Appalachian strippable coal reserves on slopes greater than 20 degrees amount to:

- less than 30 percent of Appalachian strippable coal reserves;[15]
- less than 3 percent of total Appalachian coal reserves;
- about 4 percent of total U.S. strippable reserves;
- about 0.1 percent of total U.S. recoverable coal.

Surface mining in the Midwest (mainly Illinois, Indiana, and Western Kentucky) is on flatter terrain where reclamation appears feasible. But Midwest coal has a high sulfur content (much of it containing more than 3 percent sulfur) and must be burned in plants with sulfur oxide controls in order to meet emission standards.

Most Western coal has a low sulfur content and therefore appears attractive for meeting air quality standards, even for use in Midwestern and Eastern power plants. In the past the high cost of shipping made the Western coal too expensive, but fuel oil is so expensive now that shipping costs are no longer prohibitive. But the use of Western coal is still limited by four factors: the rate at which new Western mines can be opened; railroad capacity; the fact that boilers in Eastern or Midwestern coal-fired power plants must be modified to burn Western coal; and, reclamation problems.

The reclamation issue is an unresolved problem for Western coal. An EPP-sponsored study by the National Academy of Sciences[17] points out that in many parts of the West where the rainfall is less than ten inches annually and where soils cannot retain moisture, reclamation is not feasible. The study concludes that if the best available technologies were applied, stable revegetation could likely be established in certain areas which are favored with good soil and adequate rainfall. Favorable conditions appear to exist in the mixed grass region of the Northern Great Plains and the Ponderosa pine and mountain shrub zone of the Rockies. These areas contain about 60 percent of the surface minable coal reserves in the Western United States. In these areas the NAS estimates that reclamation would add only a few cents a ton to the price of coal. But the success of rehabilitation would depend on an intensive coordinated effort that has never been made anywhere in the United States and would require strong new federal and state laws.

Water scarcity is a major factor limiting the development of coal conversion industries in the West. The NAS study[17] concludes that while there may be adequate water for mining and rehabilitation of many areas, there is not enough water available there for large scale operations like gasifying and liquefying coal or generating electric power. Another study now in progress should provide new information on the water resources availability problem.[18]

We have mentioned that trace element air pollution is associated with small particles in the burning of fossil fuels. Coal is a leading example. The trace element content appears to vary from one kind of coal to another and from one coal-bearing region to another. Several of these trace elements* appear to be associated with the inorganic sulfur in coal,[19] so that possible health hazards would be greater for high-sulfur coals, like those in the Midwest. Two other trace elements

---

* Lead, antimony, zinc, mercury, arsenic, cadmium, nickel.

(beryllium and selenium) generally occur in greatest concentrations with Appalachian coals, and in lowest concentrations with Western coals. Regional variations of some important trace elements (like fluorine) have not yet been assessed. Such regional differences may be important in shaping a coal use strategy. Standards for trace element emissions need to be formulated, and research must be carried out on their control. For the trace elements linked with sulfur, removing the sulfur from the fuel before burning can effectively reduce the trace element content.[19] Other techniques for removing trace metals are under development.[20]

Another pollution problem of high-sulfur coal which is yet unsolved is acid mine drainage, where sulfuric acid leached from exposed coal seams (in both surface and underground mines) contaminates surface and ground waters. A Department of the Interior estimate in 1969 indicated that capital costs for abatement and control of acid mine drainage at that time would amount to $6.6 billion.[21]

From an environmental perspective, there is no entirely satisfactory way to use coal in the near term. Growth in coal use until the early 1980s might best be accommodated by a mix of Western, Midwestern and Appalachian surface-mined coal. Such growth should be restricted to areas where reclamation appears feasible. In Appalachia, this means avoiding steep slopes. Regulations should be adopted for committing the best available technology to reclamation. When stack gas sulfur removal technologies are available, high-sulfur coal can be burned. Should it prove necessary to grant variances to allow burning high-sulfur coal, this use should be coupled with requirements for implementing stack gas controls.

After 1985, such controls are likely to be widely available; this will remove a major constraint on the use of plentiful high-sulfur Midwestern and Eastern coal. Less hazardous highly mechanized underground mining methods can be ready for use if R&D efforts are vigorously pursued now. Still, the small-particle air pollution problem may prove to be an environmental limiting factor on coal use. At this stage of our study it appears to us that the optimal environmental strategy for coal extraction after 1985 would involve:

- Eastern low slope and Midwestern surface mines with planned reclamation;
- underground mines with improved mining safety conditions (perhaps highly mechanized);

- Western surface mines in areas where reclamation looks feasible.

Oil

A potential for oil spills exists in drilling and recovery operations on the Outer Continental Shelf, in transporting Alaskan oil from the Trans-Alaska Pipeline (TAPS) by tanker down to the lower forty-eight states, and in importing oil by tanker. Table 3 shows the relative risks of oil spills linked to each of these options.[22]

It can be seen that the more important problems for the United States are OCS development and the tanker link for the Trans-Alaska Pipeline. The data also show that oil imports give rise to oil spills, not only in our own waters, but worldwide. In and around U.S. waters, imports contribute less spillage than OCS development does. But spillage from our imports is substantial in the waters of the rest of the world. Most of the volume of spills from both OCS operations and imports is likely to arise from major catastrophic accidents, not from everyday routine operations.

There is considerable controversy and only limited knowledge about the harmful biological effects of oil spills. An EPP commissioned study on the ecological effects of oil pollution in the marine environment provides some insights.[23] Immediate effects are clear: thousands of birds perish, and if the spill is in shallow water, shellfish also die in large numbers. But immediate mortality is only part of the problem. There is also evidence of longer term effects on marine life. Three special environments—polar regions, estuaries and tropical coral reefs—appear to be particularly vulnerable to harm. Experts are sharply divided about the severity and permanency of biological damage from oil spills. The oil industry generally holds the view that effects are not great in the long run, but there is much counter evidence. Considerably more research is needed before the risks can be fully assessed.

The EPP commissioned another oil spill study to provide an overview of present technology and future prospects for prevention, control, and clean-up of oil spills.[24] This study points out that prevention technology is, by and large, quite good. Clean-up technology is less successful. It is virtually impossible at present to contain and remove spilled oil when waves higher than three feet and/or currents of more than one knot are present. Chemical dispersants may have

Table 3. Quantities of Potential Oil Spills and Discharges into U.S. and World Waters*

Source	Major Accidents	Minor and Moderate Spills	Ballast or Waste Water Treatment[a]	Total
Outer Continental Shelf	280 to 1060[b]	52[c]	18[d]	350 to 1,130
Trans Alaska Pipeline	68[e] to 384[f]	6[g]	26[h] to 540[i]	100 to 416 (ballast treatment[a]) 614 to 930 (100% LOT[a])
Imports				
U.S. waters	68[e]	3[j]	0[k]	71
World's waters	384[f]	6[g]	540[i]	930[l] to 2,100[m]

*Oil (in barrels per day) likely to be spilled and discharged for each 2,000,000 barrels per day produced and transported.

[a]Chronic oil pollution from tank cleaning operations can be reduced by use of load-on-top (LOT) tank cleaning operations or by use of ballast treatment facilities. Most of the world's large tankers use the LOT technique.

[b]Based on 1964–1971 experience on the OCS, 280 is from USGS data.

[c]Based on 1971 Coast Guard spill data for offshore facilities in U.S. waters.

[d]Based on 1971 Gulf of Mexico OCS data.

[e]Based on 1964–1971 experience in and around U.S. waters.

[f]Based on 1969–1970 worldwide casualty analysis.

[g]Based on 1971 Coast Guard spill data for tankers (twice because moving between two ports).

[h]Ballast treatment facility with an effluent of 20 parts per million.

[i]100% LOT tankers

[j]Based on 1971 Coast Guard spill data for tankers.

[k]No ballast or waste water treatment is needed in U.S. ports.

[l]Excludes pollution from foreign offshore production.

[m]Includes pollution from foreign offshore production.

Source: D. E. Kash et al., *Energy Under the Ocean*, University of Oklahoma Press, Norman, 1973.

harmful side effects that are worse than the effects of the oil itself. Research and development on better oil spill technology should be given high priority.

Oil Shale

The Green River Formation located in Colorado, Utah and Wyoming is the most promising region for shale oil production. This formation alone contains about 600 billion barrels of oil trapped in highgrade deposits;*[25] this compares with estimated U.S. recoverable petroleum resources of about 500 billion barrels.[26]

Oil shale development raises serious environmental problems. The shale may be surface-mined, extracted from conventional underground mines, or processed *in situ* underground.** With surface or conventional underground mining, it is very difficult to dispose of huge quantities of spent shale (larger in volume than before the oil was extracted). Revegetation of the spoil is difficult; it may be impossible within a period as short as ten years. The waste disposal and revegetation problems can be largely avoided through the *in situ* process, but disturbance of underground aquifers and contamination of ground water remain difficult problems for all processes.

Large amounts of water would be needed for commercial operations in a region where water resources are limited. But water requirements for producing oil from shale are only one-third of what is required to produce liquid fuels from coal,[17, 25] and are probably still less if the *in situ* process is used.

Nuclear Power

Nuclear fission power today supplies less than 5 percent of our electric energy, but it is rapidly becoming a more important source. The U.S. Atomic Energy Commission expects nuclear installed generating capacity to increase twelve to fifteen times in 1985 and three to four times more between 1985 and 2000. Its use poses serious environmental issues, including reactor safety, radioactive waste management, and nuclear theft. Nuclear risks are qualitatively very different from those of fossil fuel systems. Like coal- or oil-fired plants, nuclear

---

* High grade deposits are defined to be at least 10 feet thick and to contain 25 or more gallons per ton.
** With the *in situ* method the rock is fractured underground with explosives or other means, and the shale is heated in place to separate the oil from the rock.

plants produce thermal pollution, but in their day-to-day operation they produce no air pollution in the usual sense. Radioactive emissions can be, and have been kept to low levels. Moreover, land use problems are small when compared to coal. To produce a given amount of electricity, about 80 times more land must be surface-mined for coal as for uranium.

But nuclear power has unique problems and uncertainties. Radio-active wastes from power plants are deadly materials that must be isolated from the environment for hundreds, sometimes hundreds of thousands, of years. Significant releases of these materials in serious accidents could cause widespread contamination and the loss of many lives. Such accidents could occur not only at power plants, but also in other parts of the fuel cycle: during truck or rail shipments of intensely radioactive spent reactor fuel to reprocessing centers,[27, 28] at the fuel reprocessing plants themselves, and at the repositories where separated radioactive wastes must be stored[29, 30] and isolated from the environment until their radioactivity decays to harmless levels. The chances of such occurrences are low. But a serious accident could be catastrophic, and its impact would be long lasting.

Another problem posed by large-scale use of nuclear power is the potential for theft of nuclear materials and their use by criminals or political extremist groups to make atom bombs or weapons that disperse dangerous radioactive materials, like plutonium. The EPP commissioned a recent study on the risks of nuclear theft and measures to prevent it.[31] The study concludes that the present system of safeguarding against theft is incomplete and offers proposals for reducing the risks.

As with all catastrophic occurrences, it is difficult to estimate the likelihood of serious nuclear accidents. Most such nuclear accidents would depend on unpredictable human error or aberrant actions; the potential for acts of sabotage is especially hard to quantify.

AEC officials have stated that the chances of a major accident occurring are about one in a million per reactor-year of operation.[32] However, a recent AEC Task Force Report points out that this level of safety cannot be assured today:

". . . Considering the large number of reactors predicted to be operational by the year 2000, and in view of the overall incident record over the past several years combined with the common mode failures that have been identified, the Task Force believes that continuing actions need to be taken to provide . . . assurance that the probability for such an accident will be one in a million or less per reactor year."[33]

One independent scientific group concludes[34] that the risk may be substantially greater than that given by the AEC. It is not now possible to provide a defensible estimate of what the true reactor accident risk is. Unfortunately, the ability to estimate this accident risk is not apt to improve much with more study. There are, and will be, too many uncertainties.

The wisdom of a commitment to nuclear power ultimately rests on the capability of our technology and institutions to manage, perhaps indefinitely, a very hazardous enterprise. This problem has been eloquently formulated by Dr. Alvin Weinberg, former director of the Oak Ridge National Laboratory:

"We nuclear people have made a Faustian bargain with society. On the one hand, we offer—in the catalytic nuclear burner—an inexhaustible source of energy . . . This source of energy, when properly handled, is almost non-polluting. But the price that we demand of society for this magical energy source is both a vigilance and a longevity of our social institutions that we are quite unaccustomed to.

"We make two demands. The first, which I think is the easier to manage, is that we exercise in nuclear technology the very best techniques and that we use people of high expertise and purpose. Quality assurance is the phrase that permeates much of the nuclear community these days. It connotes using the highest standards of engineering design and execution; of maintaining proper discipline in the operation of nuclear plants in the face of the natural tendency to relax as a plant becomes older and more familiar; . . . in short, of creating a continuing tradition of meticulous attention to detail. The second demand is less clear, and I hope it may prove to be unnecesary. This is the demand for longevity in human institutions. We have relatively little problem dealing with wastes if we can assume always that there will be intelligent people around to cope with eventualities we have not thought of."[35]

Dr. Weinberg feels that society can meet these challenges and that the benefits of nuclear power are well worth the necessary commitment. Others[36, 37] are much more pessimistic about the capabilities of our human institutions. Reasonable men differ substantially in these judgments.

There is a growing concern in the United States and the world about the wisdom of a commitment to nuclear power. But the issue of whether to continue with the growth of nuclear power cannot be resolved in isolation from other energy considerations. What is known about the risks and benefits of nuclear power must be weighed against alternative courses of action. Our analysis on alternative energy scenarios (see Section 7) shows that as long as this nation continues on a track of rapid growth in energy, nuclear fission energy will be needed to meet demand. Only under a long term commitment to substantial energy conservation could curtailment of nuclear power growth be taken seriously.

SECTION 5

Federal Energy Resources

As with foreign relations and environmental issues, we have singled out government policies for management of publicly-owned energy resources for separate discussion. These policy questions are of immediate importance, because of their magnitude and long-term effects, and they should become matters of widespread public concern.

The federal government is in a unique position to shape future patterns of national energy policy through control of publicly owned energy resources. With the Department of the Interior acting as custodian, the American people own the bulk of the remaining fossil fuel resources in the United States. These resources include an estimated 35 percent of the oil and gas, 50 percent of the coal, and 85 percent of the oil shale. Substantial amounts of the domestic uranium and geothermal steam resources are also under federal control. Although important energy resources are to be found under private and state-owned lands, the federal government controls the major portion of the nation's energy resources which are most attractive for early development, particularly offshore oil and gas on the Outer Continental Shelf, and low-sulfur coal reserves in the West.

The manner in which the government meets its obligation to the public in managing the development of publicly owned resources is critical. The Energy Policy Project has under way a staff analysis of the policies for management of these resources and their place in shaping national energy policy. This policy analysis is not yet complete, but some of the major issues are quite clear.

The pace at which the federal lands are opened can play a key role in determining the overall rate of energy growth, the mix of fuels, and the degree to which the nation must rely on imports. A policy of massive leasing of these resources would signal a future based on high rates of energy consumption. On the other hand, decisions to limit development of one or more of these resources, coupled with policies of energy conservation, could lead the nation toward lower energy growth.

The existing system for management of the public's resources works against considering such options. Each resource is subject to different laws and administrative policies, established at different times to serve varying goals and interests. But, primarily, the system for the "disposal" of most of these resources was designed through law, regulation and tradition to encourage resource development. The government has been increasingly involved in determining when and under what conditions publicly owned resources are leased for private exploitation; but once the resources are leased, the Interior Department has had only limited success in insuring development. And, until recently, there has been only the most nominal recognition of other social goals.

The Interior Department's current stated objective is to reconcile three competing social goals: insure a fair return to the public from the sale or lease of these resource, protect the environment in the process, and develop the resources in a timely and orderly manner. But the present leasing system's inherent weaknesses make this objective unachievable. Two of the major leasing programs, coal and offshore oil and gas, illustrate this problem.

While the methods vary depending on the specific resource and the laws governing its disposal, most federal resources are sold to the highest bidder through a competitive, cash-bonus bidding system. Leases for on-shore resources in "unknown" areas are given without competition and bonuses. In both instances, the lessee pays a royalty to the government as the resource is produced.

Since 1954 the leasing of oil and gas on the Outer Continental Shelf (generally defined as those offshore lands owned by the federal government and lying beyond three miles) has been the highest priority energy resource program within the government. Leasing has been confined almost entirely to the Gulf of Mexico, with some production in the Santa Barbara Channel off Southern California. Consideration is now being given to opening new lease areas offshore, in the Atlantic and the Gulf of Alaska.

Since a five-year lease schedule went into effect in 1971, lease sales for offshore areas have been held at the rate of two per year. The average annual acreage leased has nearly doubled—from 556,716 acres per year during the 1960–1969 period to 929,382 during the 1972–1973 period. The average bonus paid has risen steadily since 1970, averaging about $3,000 per acre in recent sales—almost six times the average during the previous decade. The average number of bidders per tract has steadily increased during this period.

There is evidence to suggest that the goal of achieving a fair return to the public from the leasing of these resources has been reasonably well served. But serious questions arise regarding the other goals: protection of the environment and orderly and timely development of the resources.

Several major blowouts and fires have occurred at OCS platforms in the Gulf of Mexico. The effects on the marine environment of chronic, long term oil seepage from operations and pipelines continue to be poorly understood. During this period the courts have found lack of compliance with the National Environmental Policy Act because of inadequacies in the environmental evaluation of OCS activities.

In addition, no means have been created to ascertain what rate of leasing is necessary to meet the nation's energy needs. The lease schedule itself is based on a simple extrapolation of past demand trends. Supply from the OCS is seen by the Interior Department as an attempt to fill the gap between other supply sources and the assumed demand.

Early in 1974 the President ordered a tenfold increase (to 10 million acres) by 1975 in the amount of acreage leased annually. Whether competition for the tracts will remain high with so much acreage being offered and whether a fair return to the public can be maintained under such conditions seems highly questionable. Ensuring adequate environmental controls and effective state and public participation in decision-making also appears dubious. Lack of good resource information is the most pressing issue.

Presently, all new leasing is in the Gulf of Mexico. One sale is proposed for offshore Southern California in 1975. While anticipated reserves in these areas are large, the big question marks are the areas off the Atlantic Coast and the Gulf of Alaska. Both are regarded as promising, but neither has yet been drilled. There is growing evidence to indicate the possibility of large deposits. In undeveloped offshore areas such as these the government has only limited geophysical information to aid it in its leasing decisions. Almost all of this information has been purchased from companies which have done the work for industry.

In order to properly understand anticipated production from the OCS and to ensure a fair return to the public for leased resources under an accelerated leasing schedule, it is essential for government to have the best possible understanding of potential oil and gas resources. The Interior Department's Geological Survey has attempted to expand and improve its programs related to OCS leasing; yet industry data continues to be far more extensive, as a rule, than the government's. In short, the government's understanding of what it owns is grossly inadequate.

Development of federal coal presents similar problems. Vast recoverable reserves of low-sulfur Western federal coal (estimated at 22 billion tons) are presently committed to industry. Yet in 1972 only 10 million tons of this coal was produced, amounting to a mere 2 percent of total national production. Less than 10 percent of the existing leases are presently being developed. There are no mandatory production requirements, and many leases are held in speculation of higher future fuel prices. Many of the leases already in effect contain only minimal requirements for environmental protection. Some of these are in arid or semi-arid regions where, according to a study by the National Academy of Sciences,[1] it is doubtful the land can be reclaimed after surface mining. If these leases are developed without high standards for reclamation, the government will be contributing to environmental degradation rather than serving as a model for the nation.

However, given the huge amounts of coal under lease, little of which is being mined, no apparent need exists for a major new thrust in coal leasing before 1980, and in fact leasing was virtually stopped in 1971. The government does, therefore, have time to put together a rational coal leasing program.

The critical first step in such a program is to assemble an adequate data and information base. This does not exist. Coal in the West is held in complicated, intermingled ownership patterns. Much of the public coal underlies private lands. The government has poor records of its ownership of most of this coal. In many regions, the government has limited knowledge of the quality and quantity of the coal reserves that it does know it owns, and must rely on data the industry has been willing to supply to do any development planning. Information is also inadequate to support environmental planning for rehabilitation of surface-mined land and for maintenance of air and water quality, as well as for protection of range land and wildlife habitat.

Availability of water is a key issue in the use of federal western coal for coal-fired electric power plants at the mine, and coal gasification and liquefication projects. To support this projected development, huge new water storage and diversion projects will be required. There has been virtually no evaluation of how this will affect the streams and rivers of the regions or the values and uses they support. Basic water resource limitations and important legal and administrative questions must be weighed before commitments are made to massive leasing of western coal.

The potential for exploiting the vast reserves of oil shale and extensive geothermal steam resources under public control is promising but still uncertain. A limited experimental leasing program is under way to determine if oil shale and geothermal steam can be developed economically, in an environmentally acceptable manner. Unexpectedly high bids in the first sales of oil shale rights, and the considerable number of participants in the first sale of geothermal leases, indicate high industry expectation of the economic potential of these resources. But problems similar to those in coal and OCS leasing are evident.

Vastly improved planning is a necessary reform in the existing system for developing all federal energy resources. It must begin with the gathering of comprehensive information on the resources themselves. But a planning system also must include information to assess the impact of development on the environment, on other resources, and on the economy and the people of the region where development takes place.

Steps can be taken immediately to improve resource information. A program of government-funded research and exploration through contracts with private and state agencies can begin soon after it is funded. In addition, industry could be required to share its basic data with the government. But the government also needs to have a greatly enlarged capacity to assess and evaluate such data once it is obtained.

The second major step toward a revamped federal energy minerals management system is to create improved mechanisms for reconciling the different, oftentimes competing, goals of the program.

At the national level, such analysis must address the fundamental question of the role of federal resources in supplying national energy needs. For the present, the decision has been made to rapidly develop all federal energy resources simultaneously. Such a policy may make sense in some areas, but as an across-the-board proposition it represents a failure to weigh conflicting values. It will be far more difficult to ensure a fair return to the public from the leasing of its resources and to protect the environment under a program of rapid development.

Of equal importance is understanding the tradeoffs at the regional and local level. For example, any decision to permit extensive development of federal coal in the Fort Union field of Montana, Wyoming and North Dakota will significantly change the character of that part of the country.

Even under a historic trends scenario, development can be selective both by resource and by location. Where development takes place, stringent environmental protection measures can be employed. The options, of course, are greatly expanded if less development is required under lower growth assumptions. Also, through a permanent planning mechanism, the people of the development regions can be given a voice in decisions affecting their future.

In addition to reforming the existing federal resource management system, the government itself could go into the business of developing the resources. A government corporation could be formed and given the job of exploring and developing all new federally controlled resource areas. The corporation could be designed to develop a single resource such as oil shale, or to cover development of all resources in a given geographic-economic region such as the Rocky Mountain states or the OCS.

In any case—reform of the existing system, a purely private enterprise approach, or public development—government officials must start to take a hard look at how the public's energy resources are managed.

SECTION 6

The Next Few Years: Choices and Limits

IN FOREGOING SECTIONS we have examined the origins of the energy gap and have given special attention to some critical policy areas that interconnect with energy. We now consider more generally the immediate choices the nation has in responding to our present energy difficulties, the limits to those choices, and some of their consequences.

Time Constraints: How Long Will Various Solutions Take?

It takes time to make major energy dicisions or to change policies. It also requires time—usually several years—to build new facilities, to open new oil fields and mines or to change consumption habits and technologies. These time constraints affect our choices for trying to balance the nation's energy budget.

The Near Term

For the next two to four years it will not be possible to build major new energy supply facilities from start to finish. Neither will it be possible to completely rebuild homes, factories or transportation systems. During this period the nation will have to make do with the facilities already in place or in the later stages of construction. This does not imply that nothing can be done, but rather that significant impacts on energy supply and use will come through more effective use of the physical capital already in place, and through short-run conservation measures. Policymakers will also need to lay the groundwork during this period for changes to benefit the country in the more distant future.

59

The Medium Term

During the late 1970s and early 1980s, the results of the new construction, well drilling, mine openings, greater public awareness of energy conservation, and the shift to more efficient energy consumption technologies begun in the next year or two will bear fruit. These changes, for the most part, will represent the implementation of currently available technologies rather than those still in the laboratory or pilot plant stage, but they could have a profound impact on the energy situation in five to ten years. Changes in consumer behavior and preferences could also have a significant effect in this period.

The Longer Term—1985 and Beyond

In the long run, the United States is not bound in an energy straitjacket. The further one goes into the future, the broader the options, provided steps are taken now to lay the groundwork. Research and development, changes in public attitudes through public education, and establishment of better governmental energy institutions—if undertaken now—will pave the way for the new energy sources and more efficient energy consumption technologies which can come into play in this period. It must be emphasized that the R&D process is long. Frequently, new industries must be created before a new technology can be put into effect on a wide scale. Fundamentally new technologies like nuclear fusion and large scale solar power will probably count for little until after the year 2000. But changes in the mix of the gross national product could significantly affect the shape of future energy requirements in the 1985–2000 period.

Options for the Immediate Future

The nation's efforts to balance supply and demand in the next few years require a mix of policies which will create a minimum of short term dislocations and hardships while working in consonance with long term goals. Managing a transition from energy abundance to relative scarcity with minimum impact on the economy, the environment, energy prices and foreign policy objectives will be much more difficult than achieving any single goal. But balancing these multiple objectives lies at the heart of intelligent energy policies.

The interruption of some oil imports by the Arab oil embargo laid bare the gap between domestic supply and demand which was growing before the Middle East war began. As we have seen, total energy consumption was rising steadily before the crisis. The nation was demanding each year extra amounts of energy equal to one and a half million barrels of oil a day. Since 1970 virtually all this increase came from imported oil, much of it from the Middle East. By last summer, Arab oil imports amounted to about 2 million barrels per day.

The immediate problem is to use less energy and set about making more. For the near future, the choices are rather limited. The outlook for expanding domestic energy output quickly is not promising. It takes three to five years to plan and carry out a major expansion of offshore oil production, and eight to ten to construct a nuclear power plant, in contrast to some conservation measures which can take effect immediately. An additional complication is that big projects to expand supplies often entail big changes in the character of the regions where they take place—changes which may inspire considerable opposition and hence delay of these projects.

There are, however, some potential sources of supply which could expand more rapidly.

Oil Imports

Until the recent embargo, oil imports were the energy source which most government and industry planners counted on to provide the bulk of the growth in energy consumption. The Middle East nations own the oil reserves necessary to support expected world-wide growth for the next decade. If the peace negotiations and other international deliberations turn out favorably, the United States would be able to import even more oil in the future than it has in the past. How should the United States respond to this situation?

A policy of simply forsaking imports is an impractical and simplistic overreaction. Even during the embargo, the United States has continued to import more than 5 million barrels of oil per day. But greater care and selectivity are needed in planning oil imports for the future.

We must weigh the economic, political and environmental costs of imports from specific nations on a case-by-case basis. And, we must not lose sight of how our actions in world oil markets affect the well-being of nations whose welfare is linked to our own in a myriad of ways unrelated to energy questions, as discussed in Section 3.

If we import oil in prewar quantities at $10/barrel, the cost would exceed $20 billion per year, with nearly $4 billion more per year for each additional million barrels per day. The high price of imported oil alone gives great impetus to efforts toward saving energy and finding alternative sources. Yet the prospects in the next few years for reliable supplies at delivered prices much lower than $8 a barrel look dim. The oil available for expanded production in the near term lies primarily in Saudi Arabia and Iran and possibly Iraq. The production of other nations has apparently peaked out for technical, economic and political reasons.

This does not portend well for the United States or other oil importing nations. Unless a mammoth new discovery is made somewhere in the world in the next few years, or unless the smaller exporters resume growth in production, all the importing nations will be dependent on the growth in oil production of a very few countries. No matter how world oil demand responds to the recent price increases, decisions by Saudi Arabia or Iran could keep oil supplies very tight and the price high.

If the United States elects to continue to import oil, despite the implications for international relations and the economic costs, measures are needed to mitigate the impact of a possible future embargo. Central to any such program would be the establishment of some form of oil stockpile.

Stockpiling Oil

If the nation chooses to increase imports, it is incumbent on us to undertake a positive program for dealing with future cutoffs—a strategic storage program. Normal practice in the United States has been for the industry to maintain inventories of 40 to 50 days supply to deal with seasonal demands and operating requirements. This is normal working inventory, and recent experience has demonstrated that it is not adequate in the event of a sudden interruption.

The United States has two basic options should it choose to adopt a storage program. The reserves can consist either of developing oil in place and "shutting in" the field, or of buying oil and placing it in storage in salt domes and tanks. The cost of either is high. Based on studies which reflect recent oil price increases, a strategic reserve of stored oil sufficient to provide 2 million barrels per day at $10/barrel for one year (about the current level of Arab imports) would cost over $8 billion. To develop reserves in the ground with a producing capacity of 2 million barrels per day would cost on the order of $16 billion, based on an extrapolation of the cost of developing the Elk Hills Naval

Petroleum Reserve. Reserve production capacity costs more, but it could be produced for many years while the tanks would run dry in a year.

There is another difficulty besides the magnitude of the investment. Current shortages in the world market would make it hard to build up stockpiles of oil. To develop tank storage equal to a year's imports from Arab countries, the United States would have to augment its imports by one-third for one year; or else reduce overall oil consumption 10 percent for the year. It would take several years to develop the equivalent shut-in producing capacity.

There are a number of alternative approaches for developing an emergency oil supply. Since it probably would not be profitable for private capital to invest in this kind of reserve, a major government role would be needed. It could take one of the forms we have discussed, or a third option, examined by an EPP grantee,[1] might be adopted. That is to build up a strategic reserve through government contracts let on a competitive basis. This kind of program could lead to rapid development of new sources of domestic fuels, including synthetics, on a competitive basis.

The costs of developing security of supply are high, but so are the costs of a shutoff. A stockpile is, in effect, a national insurance policy.

Domestic Oil and Gas

The price of domestic crude oil has nearly doubled in the past year and the price of "new" crude has increased even more. Prices for "new" natural gas have likewise been rising under FPC control. There is reason to expect these prices to excite more drilling and increased production. Yet because of the time required to find, drill and develop new oil fields it would probably be three or four years before the results of any major new exploratory efforts could pay off. In the meantime, any increased production would have to come from existing fields and wells.

There are about 360,000 stripper wells in the United States (wells which produce less than 10 barrels per day); in aggregate they produce slightly more than 1 million barrels per day, or about 12 percent of domestic crude production. Increased crude prices could make it economical to keep these old wells producing longer and to reactivate some abandoned wells.

The use of secondary and tertiary recovery methods on existing wells—technologies which use water, heat or special solvents to extract a greater fraction of the oil in existing fields—could add to supply, with long term as well as short term benefits.

The short term response of these marginal oil supplies to the recent price hikes is still unknown. Certainly, higher oil prices will elicit some increase from these sources. But, it is important to recognize that the expanded output will first have to offset declines in production from existing fields before there can be any net increase in domestic oil production.

The U.S. Government owns Naval Petroleum Reserves, earmarked for emergency use by the military. One field which has been developed—the Elk Hills Naval Petroleum Reserve, in California—could produce on the order of 100,000 barrels of oil per day within a few months, if Congress authorizes it. Additional investments could enlarge production to more than 300,000 barrels per day within three years.

Short term increases in gas supplies in response to higher prices are harder to forecast than for oil. One possible source of marginal gas supplies is the tight gas formations* of the West. Large scale fracturing might produce gas from this source.

In three or four years, when the Alaska oil pipeline is finished, the domestic oil supply problem should be eased somewhat. Production from new fields in the Santa Barbara channel and Gulf of Mexico in the same time period could also help the domestic oil and gas situation.

Coal

Coal is often mentioned as a fallback source in times of crisis since it is abundant and its location fairly well known. Several significant constraints limit coal's ability to fulfill this promise in the near term. Labor problems, the need for improved health and safety, and shortages of the supplies needed to operate the mines all impede the rapid expansion of output from existing mines. Another impediment is that many boilers are not designed to use coal instead of scarcer oil or gas.

Paramount to any short term increase in coal output is the cooperation of the men who mine the coal. Coal miners have long-standing grievances over working conditions which have led to local work

---

* The gas in some of the Rocky Mountain formations is contained in small, unconnected pockets from which the flow is too slow to be economical.

stoppages and slowdowns. In recent years (excluding 1971, when there was a long strike) coal mines have operated 225 working days a year, which is equal to a 4½ day work week. To increase production significantly, these labor disputes would have to be settled in a fashion that would give the miners incentives to work longer hours. Even a full 5-day week could increase annual coal production by 50 million tons. This is roughly equal to 600,000 barrels of oil a day.

The chances for such a settlement are uncertain. A new United Mine Workers industry-wide contract will be negotiated in late 1974 under a new union president who is committed to improvements in working conditions. Early and thoughtful attention by all parties concerned, possibly including mediation by the federal government, could produce an amicable settlement before the contract termination date, thereby increasing coal production this year and next. On the other hand, a bitter protracted strike would seriously delay enlarging coal output. It might raise the kind of emergency Great Britain faced during the winter of 1973–74—a dire shortage of domestically produced energy.

Opening new mines, particularly strip mines, offers a second approach to increasing coal production. In the past, strip mining has provided a means of rapid expansion; from 1969 to 1971, output rose 60 million tons, from below 200 million tons per year to almost 260 million tons. Conceivably, such an increase in strip mining could be accomplished in the current crisis. Most likely it would come from relatively small mining operations in Appalachia or in the Midwest, using existing machinery. Although huge draglines are the most efficient way of removing large amounts of overburden and coal in relatively flat terrain, they take two or three years to manufacture and erect. Short term growth would require the use of existing mining machinery or general excavation equipment, like that used for highway construction.

It takes three to five years to open a new underground coal mine, and very few are opened at all, unless a purchaser stands ready to commit himself through a long-term contract to buy the lifetime output of the mine. These long-term contracts are essential to attract the substantial capital investment needed to open a large mine. But, at present, unresolved air pollution problems limit the use of coal, and make purchasers reluctant to enter into long-term contracts.

About 70 percent of the coal mined in the United States is transported by railroad. It appears that a 50 million ton per year increase, about 8 percent, in coal hauling could be accommodated with little or no difficulty by the present cars and railroads, but that further increases would require additional investment.

Finally, the main problem with using coal is air pollution. This topic was covered at length in Section 4.

Nuclear Power

Nuclear power is expected to become larger and larger in the energy economy, because units already committed and under construction equal 20 to 30 percent of the normal growth in total energy consumption for the next few years.

Based on present construction schedules, nuclear power capacity is expected to jump from 24,000 megawatts to about 60,000 megawatts between now and the end of 1976. This represents a large portion of total new energy supplies anticipated in the period. If we pursue conservation aggressively, nuclear capacity might even meet half of our growth needs in the 1970s. Yet there is real danger of slippage in this new capacity. Labor, materials, and technical problems may cause nuclear power shortages and lead to heavier demands on coal- and oil-fired power plants. Besides all this, the desirability of an aggressive commitment to nuclear power is in question, as Section 4 details.

Supplies from other sources, such as geothermal, oil shale, and solar space heating will be negligible in the next three or four years, although the groundwork for future development can be laid.

Reducing Consumption

The difficulties and uncertainties of getting more domestic supplies in the short term shift most of the burden for bridging the energy gap to lower consumption. How individual and industrial energy consumers respond to energy shortages will in large measure determine their severity. These responses will also indicate how much energy waste can be eliminated by simple 'leak plugging'' in response to higher prices and shortages. Some of the savings the nation must make, however, will require real inconveniences and hardship. Energy savings from the measures now in effect are uncertain; estimates of what they will produce range from modest to the equivalent of a year's growth in energy consumption.

Three different approaches to energy savings are possible in the time just ahead. First, consumers can make technical improvements in the way they use energy. They may add insulation and storm windows to their homes; they may buy smaller, more efficient automobiles. These adaptations have more long-term than short-term benefits because they take time or because, at the outset, they exact an energy cost to produce the energy-saving materials and devices. Putting in insulation or buying a smaller car does not take time in itself; but industry needs time to produce enough insulation and small autos for all the people who may want to buy them. In addition, expanding productive capacity to make, for example, extra insulation, means in turn short-term increases in industrial energy demand. It takes time for this energy investment to be repaid. Improving the efficiency of energy use is by all means a desirable goal; but it is not necessarily a quick fix for shortages.

A second approach to saving energy is voluntary cutbacks in response to urging by the government and energy suppliers. The country received many such exhortations during the Arab embargo and much of the subsequent reduction in consumption may be attributed to them.

The third approach is mandatory allocation and rationing. If consumers do not cut back consumption enough voluntarily, then compulsory methods are needed to make sure that everyone shares the burden equitably and no one suffers unduly.

Taking into consideration the Project's analysis of the roots of the crisis, the narrow options for increasing supplies in the short term, and the rather limited scope for saving energy through more efficient consumption in this period, it appears that shortages are here to stay for the next few years. Uncertain developments, like a resumption of Arab oil imports, could make the shortages milder and limit their duration. On the other hand, continued supply problems, coupled with worse weather, could mean real hardships. In any event, crisis, aggravation, or maybe just annoyance, seem likely for the years just ahead.

In the meantime, there are important issues of social equity that must be faced while we take action to balance our energy budget.

Short-Term Equity Problems

We believe the nation will be faced with an unaccustomed challenge for the next few years: that of sharing a limited amount of energy among competing uses, and doing it in a fair way, which the public believes is fair.

Just now, energy prices are changing more rapidly than the time it takes for consumers and producers alike to adjust to the new circumstances. This can cause major social and economic disruptions. Industrial processes and habits, which may have been profitable when energy was cheap, may suddenly be moneylosers. Cars with extravagant tastes for fuel cannot be quickly replaced. Government budgets for vital services, like police and fire departments, may not stretch to cover the fuel they need. And the lead time for enlarging supplies means that, for a time at least, the higher prices do not bring forth plenty. In the short term, price alone cannot ration the available energy, without causing major disruptions.

In these circumstances, government action is in order to control the rate of price increases and allocate shortages so as to spread the hardships as fairly as possible. The major areas for government action include:

Energy Industry Profits

An explosive short-term equity issue is that energy industry profits and prices are rising rapidly while other industries and people in general are suffering considerable hardship.

The argument is made that these profits are unearned because they arise from scarcity alone; production costs have not materially increased. The industry, in this view, is profiteering from the shortages caused by the embargo.

The industry rebuttal to these charges is that higher profits are needed for massive reinvestments in new energy facilities, and that the industry's long-term profits are only mediocre, compared with other major industries.

This issue will doubtless be the subject of heated debate for some time. A possible approach is to remove the industry's existing special tax benefits but refrain from imposing a new tax.[2] The relationship between energy prices, industry profitability, and the ability to attract capital in the petroleum and electric utility industries is under study by an EPP grantee[3] and will be the subject of a forthcoming report.

Income and Employment Effects

Major increases in energy prices (or any basic necessity) have a disproportionate effect on the budgets of lower income people.[4] Various approaches have been put forward to deal with this problem, which is really a consequence of the basic patterns of income distribution in this country—a vital issue in its own right. Specific energy policy measures might deal narrowly with energy prices and their impact on the broader problem of income distribution. One approach is price controls. To the extent that they can be enforced, they keep prices down, but at a cost. They interfere with the normal price incentives to all consumers (not just the poor) to use less, and to producers to provide more. A more direct and more effective approach to compensating lower income groups would be to pay an outright energy subsidy to people who qualify, in a fashion similar to the food stamp program.

The most important energy effects on equity and income are loss of jobs from sudden supply disruption. The recent shifts in auto production from plants producing large cars to plants producing small cars, and the resulting layoffs, are the most publicly visible employment effects of the current shortage. Less well known are the layoffs that have hit retail car dealers, service station employees and other auto related establishments. In addition, recreation industries that depend on auto and airline travel are suffering; the airlines themselves were among the first industries affected, as were the trucking industry and recreational vehicle producers. Among the less visible effects of the current crisis are the employee cutbacks in industries that depend on petrochemicals; these include plastics, textiles, and furniture manufacturers.

The U.S. Bureau of Labor Statistics reported in January that the unemployment rate increased from 4.6 to 5.2 percent between October 15, 1973, and January 15, 1974. This increase amounts to 600,000 workers. About 200,000 of these layoffs, the BLS estimates, were due directly to the energy crisis. While estimates vary as to the final employment effects during 1974, uncertainty and anxiety over job losses is likely to continue throughout the following months. An attempt to provide a basis for projecting employment effects of alternative energy scenarios is a major Energy Policy Project staff study.[5] This study was undertaken to develop new information about the role of energy-intensive and nonenergy-intensive industries within the overall economy and within the labor force.

While the study's principal emphasis has been on long-run trend changes, it bases its analysis on a detailed understanding of energy, employment, and economic growth trends of the past two decades. The results of the study will be presented in our final report.

SECTION 7

Looking Forward

Introduction to Scenarios

The easiest way to analyze energy policy is backward, through hindsight. Unfortunately, we have to live it forward. Many an energy study has tried to deal with the opaque future by extrapolating forward the trends of the present or the recent past. In our work for the Project, we have chosen to regard the future a little differently.

We believe that the future, though full of surprises, is in some measure within our control. Choices we make now will shape that future. In order to illuminate the range of choices the Project has developed a method of analyzing the long-term implications of present energy decisions. We have constructed three plausible but very different energy futures for the period through the year 2000, as shown in Figures 5 and 6.

The alternative futures, or scenarios, are based on different assumptions we have made about the energy growth patterns our society might adopt for the years ahead, and the policies and consequences that each would entail. Of course, an infinite number of futures is possible; and it is most unlikely that the real energy future of the United States will conform closely to any of the three scenarios we have chosen to describe. They are not predictions, but a tool for rigorous thinking. We do not advocate one option over the others but present each for comparative analysis by the reader.

Our first scenario, which we call *historical growth,* assumes that the use of energy will continue to grow much as it has in the past. It

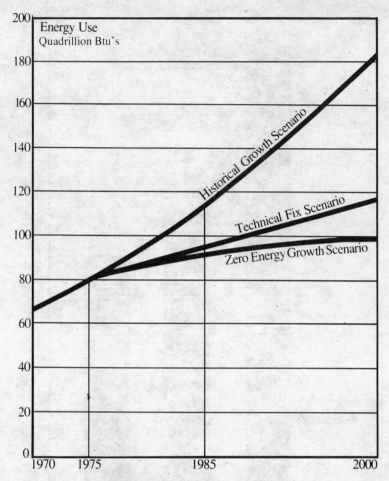

Figure 5. Scenarios at a Glance

assumes that the nation will not deliberately impose any policies that might affect our ingrained habits of energy use, but will make a strong effort to develop supplies at a rapid pace to match rising demand.

Early results suggest that this energy future is indeed possible, even with domestic resources alone, through the year 2000. It would require very aggressive development of all our possible supplies—oil and gas onshore and offshore, coal, shale, nuclear power. If it proved feasible to increase oil imports on a large scale, then the pressure on domestic resources would relax somewhat. Still, the political, eco-

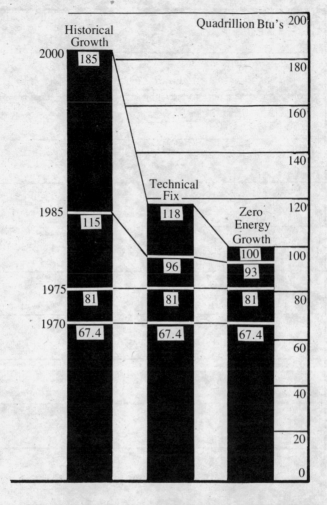

Figure 6. Energy Consumption, Three Scenarios

nomic and environmental problems of getting that much energy out
of the earth would be formidable.

Our *technical fix* scenario shares with *historical growth* a similar
level and mix of goods and services. But it reflects a determined,
conscious national effort to reduce demand for energy through the
application of energy-saving technologies. Our work so far has re-
vealed that the slower rate of energy growth in *technical fix*—about

half as high as *historical growth's*—permits more flexibility of energy supply, but still provides a quality of life at home, travel convenience, and economic growth that, to our minds at least, differs little from the *historical growth* scenario.

It would be possible to eliminate growth in at least one of the major domestic sources of energy—Rocky Mountain coal or shale, or nuclear power, or oil and gas—and still meet the energy growth rates of this scenario.

Zero energy growth is different. It represents a real break with our accustomed ways of doing things. Yet it does not represent austerity. It would give everyone in the United States more energy benefits in the year 2000 than he enjoys today, even enough to allow the less privileged to catch up to the comforts of the American Way of Life. It does not preclude economic growth.

It might come about if society became concerned enough about the social and environmental costs of energy growth, and if technology seemed unable to solve these problems. It might also reflect broader social concerns, like uneasiness about the dehumanizing aspects of big centralized institutions. *Zero energy growth* would emphasize durability, not disposability of goods. It would substitute for the idea that "more is better," the ethic that "enough is best."

All three scenarios share certain characteristics. They all assume household comforts and conveniences greater than today's; no one must live, because of energy scarcity, in a lightless shack or a sweltering tenement. Every American would have a warm home in winter, air conditioning in hot climates, a kitchen complete with appliances. He would still drive a car and have a job although he might drive less or have a different job depending on the scenario the nation follows.

The growth rates were not arbitrarily chosen. They represent a sum of the growth we have postulated in all the energy-using components of our society. All the scenarios use the Census Bureau's forecasts of population and households;[1] the forecasts for segments like transportation, home appliances, industrial use, and so on were developed by our staff for *historical growth* and modified for the other scenarios.

Our work on the scenarios is not yet complete, particularly in the area of the interplay between economic forces and energy growth. Yet we have learned enough from our work so far that a sketch of it in this preliminary report may broaden today's energy dialogue.

Resuming Historical Growth in Energy Consumption

The nation has the option of resuming its consumption growth over the next 25 years at a rate approximating the average for 1950–1972—3.4 percent per year. Energy consumption could grow from 75 quadrillion Btu's in 1973 to about 95 in 1980, 115 in 1985, and 185 quadrillion Btu's in 2000.

The primary emphasis of this scenario is in developing and producing sufficient energy supplies to meet the growth in consumption. Preliminary results from a study by Resources For the Future (RFF)[2] indicate that enough energy could be produced to meet historical growth demand between now and 2000 providing that institutional constraints did not prevent it. Decisions, especially those involving the environmental impacts and foreign policy problems of one energy source relative to another, could shift the supply mix heavily in favor of either domestic fossil fuels, nuclear power or imported oil. Relative prices will also play a key role. At the same time, it is clear that significant increases in output from all major domestic sources would be required if energy consumption were to resume the historic growth rate. The RFF conclusions are based primarily on an econometric analysis of past production in response to price rather than a detailed technical projection of future production rates. The production was, however, compared to a variety of resource estimates.

Figure 7 depicts the likely consumption patterns of energy consumption in the *historical growth* scenario and is the base from which savings in the other scenarios are estimated.

Three possible supply cases are depicted in Figure 8. The first case involves continued growth of oil imports so that they provide all of the growth in oil and about 20 percent of the overall growth in energy. The other two cases reflect major long term efforts to achieve domestic self-sufficiency in energy. The second case assumes that domestic oil and gas resources are available at reasonable prices so that the nation can continue to depend on these fuels as the primary source of energy for the remainder of this century and well into the 21st century. The third reflects the opposite assumption that oil and gas resources are either so limited or costly that we must shift to coal and nuclear power for most of the growth.

The achievement of any of these supply cases, and in fact the scenario as a whole, requires that environmental and safety concerns be met with modest increases in cost and that major expansions of any

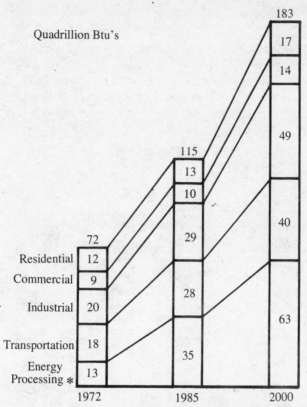

Quadrillion Btu's

183
17
14
49

115
13
10

40

72
Residential 12
Commercial 9
29

Industrial 20
28
40

Transportation 18
35
63

Energy
Processing * 13

1972   1985   2000

Figure 7. Energy Consumption Pattern In Historical Growth Scenario

* Energy processing—electric generation and transmission losses, oil refining, gas processing, uranium enrichment.

energy source not be effectively blocked through moratoriums on new construction or by outright prohibitions. In addition, the scenario requires either that the government permit basic fuel prices to rise to the levels needed to bring forth the supplies indicated, that sufficient subsidies be provided to the industry to accomplish the same ends, or that the federal government itself explore and develop the energy resources.

The potential for oil imports and the problems associated with future dependence on them for a significant fraction of energy growth are discussed in Sections 3 and 6.

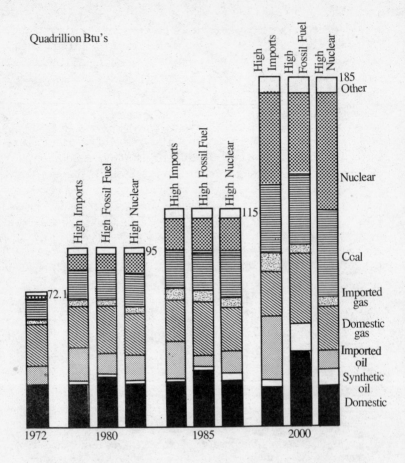

Quadrillion Btu's

Figure 8. Supply Options in Historical Growth Scenario

Long-term dependence on oil and gas raises the question of resource availability. It is a question that is very difficult to answer because the only definitive information on oil and gas in the ground comes from drilling wells. The result of this information is known as "proven reserves," while much larger resource estimates are based on geological inferences. Certain undrilled geological formations are similar to other oil and gas producing formations so it is reasonable to assume that they contain oil and gas.

One widely held view frequently ascribed to M. King Hubbert,[3] an eminent geologist, holds that oil and gas are limited resources which will certainly peak out within the next few decades and run out rapidly thereafter. Based on this view, some conclude that the United States and in fact the whole world should stop burning oil and gas as soon as possible, saving these resources for non-energy uses, especially for fertilizers and petrochemical feed stocks.

The opposing view, based on historical precedents and geological inference, is that there is a good deal more oil and gas to be found if the price is right and the industry responds accordingly. The resource availability controversy can be settled only by future exploration for oil and gas. The work done for the Project by RFF suggests that energy resources are at least sufficient to meet the year 2000 requirements with major reliance on oil and gas supply. Shale oil, synthetic petroleum from coal and alternative sources could also be developed by 2000.

Whether or not the nation should continue its heavy dependence on oil and gas and other finite fuels for the remainder of the century depends on how long they can be produced at reasonable cost. In the medium term, however, the key question is how fast domestic production can be enlarged, not how long these resources will last.

The supply case using coal and nuclear power does not raise the same resource questions, particularly if nuclear breeder technology is perfected. Its main problems are environmental, as have been discussed in Section 4.

In addition to the political, economic, resource and environmental uncertainties in supplying *historical growth,* there is the question of higher energy prices and their effect on consumption. Will consumers buy and use the amount of energy in this scenario at the prices now anticipated or will they reduce their consumption still further? The 3.4 percent per year growth in this scenario is significantly less than the 4 to 5 percent experienced during the late 1960s and early 1970s, but it still approximates growth in the 1945–65 period, a time when prices were lower and much more stable than they are apt to be in the future.

This *historical growth* scenario would require a few basic policy decisions in the near future which would then be followed by some detailed implementation plans.

(1) The government would have to emphasize expanded energy supplies in its actions rather than stressing active measures to promote conservation. Continued subsidies to limit increases in the price of energy may be needed. Demand would also be stimulated by a con-

tinuation of economic growth along current patterns. Policies generally favoring energy-intensive private automobiles, detached housing, and energy-intensive industries might be needed while government funding for mass transit or new housing construction to save energy would receive a lower priority.

The tools available for subsidizing the cost of energy were discussed in Section 2.

(2) The nation would have to develop *all* the major sources of energy growth—oil imports, OCS oil and gas, Rocky Mountain shale and coal and nuclear power—in the near and medium term. Even so, it is possible to forego vigorous development of one of the options over the longer term if the others are pushed more aggressively. For example, under this scenario a reduction in imports leading to self-sufficiency in the late 1980s is possible. Or, development of *one* of the following could be slowed but not eliminated: oil and gas development on the Atlantic and Pacific OCS, Rocky Mountain fossil fuel production or nuclear power. To do so would require pushing the other three options very hard, as shown in the alternative supply cases depicted in Figure 8.

(3) Exploration and development of oil and gas would have to be encouraged by favorable government price, tax, and federal leasing policies. To get the large quantities required in the domestic oil and gas supply case, it would be essential to develop the Atlantic and Pacific Outer Continental Shelves (OCS), Alaska, the Gulf of Mexico, and the Alaskan OCS rapidly. Development of Western oil shale would have to be pushed as well. This raises the federal leasing problems discussed in Section 5 and the environmental and regional development problems indicated in Section 4. Greater reliance on imported oil could ease some of these pressures, but it would require the construction of super-ports and would subject the coastal waters to oil spills and coastal industrialization similar to that which would accompany OCS production.

(4) Increased coal use requires resolution of the strip mining and air pollution problems discussed in Section 4 as well as the labor and economic problems noted in Section 6. With the anticipated prices for oil and gas, coal should have no problem competing with them on an economic basis but the environmental question would have to be resolved.

(5) Significant growth in nuclear power is required in this scenario no matter which supply case is selected. A twelve to fifteen times

increase in on-line nuclear capacity between now and 1985 is projected, based on the large number of plants now on order or under construction. It would be followed by an additional three to fourfold increase by the year 2000, depending on the degree to which transportation is switched to electric power and the extent to which coal could be used to fuel electric power growth. Thus, questions of nuclear power safety, safeguarding nuclear materials and handling of radioactive wastes would have to be resolved. To achieve the necessary rate of energy supply growth would require that design, siting, and federal licensing procedures for individual power plants be streamlined and standardized and that other elements in the nuclear power fuel cycle such as enrichment, reprocessing and waste handling proceed apace.

(6) All of the supply options for this scenario require extremely large investments in refineries, power plants, pipelines, transmission lines and other large facilities. The capital requirements are large in comparison with other investments made by the economy, and may need to grow. This problem is the subject of a Project-sponsored study by Jerome Hass[4] of Cornell University. Serious siting, technical manpower, and construction labor problems also arise in addition to the capital problem. Unless speedy solutions are found to this broad class of problems the scenario would not be achieved.

(7) Research and development programs which concentrate on enhancing energy supply and conversion technology and on environmental clean-up are crucial to the *historical growth* scenario. The effort would emphasize medium-term technologies rather than fundamentally new, long-term technologies.

Technical Fix Scenario

A second model of the future offers the option of reducing energy demand substantially below historical growth rates. This is accomplished by making consumption efficiency, rather than increased supply, the focal point of energy policy.

The scenario under discussion was developed by applying economically feasible energy-saving "technical fixes" to the end uses of energy in the *historical growth* scenario. As a result, energy demand grows at half the 3.4 percent rate in the *historical growth* scenario, but without reducing the standard of living or significantly changing lifestyles.

Figure 9 shows the magnitude of the energy savings in the major

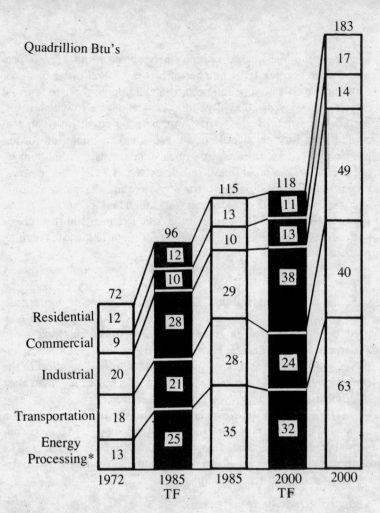

Figure 9. Energy Consumption Patterns: Technical Fix vs. Historical Growth.

* Energy processing—electric generation and transmission losses, oil refining, gas processing, uranium enrichment.

categories of use by 1985 and 2000 if the conservation efforts are begun in the near future. The total possible energy savings by 2000 in the *technical fix* scenario are about 65 quadrillion Btu's per year —one-third of the energy consumed in the *historical growth* scenario and almost as much as our total energy consumption today. Figures 10, 11 and 12 highlight the specific technical solutions which make

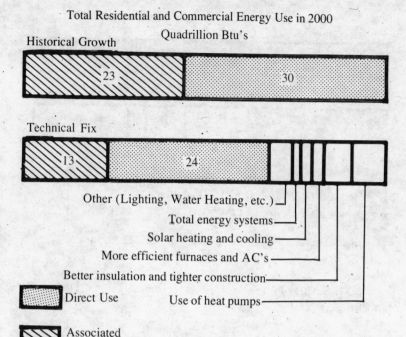

Total Residential and Commercial Energy Use in 2000
Quadrillion Btu's

Figure 10. Residential and Commercial Savings, Technical Fix vs. Historical Growth

these savings possible in each of the major energy-consuming sectors.

We have estimated each of these savings on the basis of outside studies and work by staff members. These estimates are technically feasible. The conservation technologies specified appear to us to be economically feasible as well, on the basis of calculations that take into account both initial and operating costs.

Technical Opportunities for Savings

Although there are a large number of ways in which to cut energy consumption without reducing our standard of living or the benefits we receive from energy, the greatest savings come from a relatively few—space heating and cooling, industrial process heat production and automobiles. Detailed descriptions of all of the energy conservation measures used in the *technical fix* scenario will be presented in the final report, but the most important ones are highlighted here.

Reducing the energy required to heat and cool homes and com-

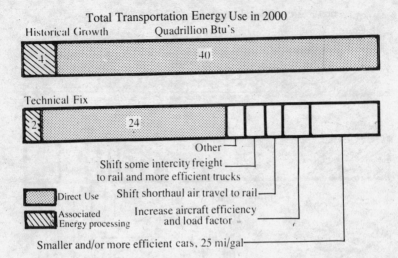

Figure 11. Savings in Transportation, Technical Fix vs. Historical Growth

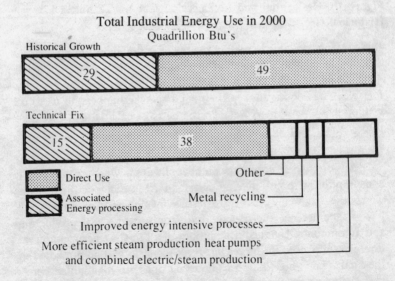

Figure 12. Industrial Savings, Technical Fix vs. Historical Growth

mercial buildings involves three different but complementary approaches: improved building design and construction so that less heating and cooling are required; more efficient systems for heating and cooling; and the use of renewable sources such as the sun. In the first instance, more widespread use of insulation and double glazing can be combined with construction of "tighter" buildings so that outside air does not leak in. These relatively simple approaches already pass the test of technical and economic feasibility.

The heat pump is the best example of a more efficient heating system. Heat pumps are electric or heat operated refrigerators or air conditioners operating in reverse. They warm the house by cooling the out-of-doors. They use mechanical energy, generally from electric motors, to bring *in* the "free" but low temperature energy in the natural environment and pump it up to useful temperatures. For every Btu a heat pump consumes in electricity, it produces two or three in heating for a house. This compares with the one Btu of energy provided by electric resistance heaters for every Btu they consume. The use of the heat pump for space heating, and cooling when they are reversed, has to date been economically feasible only in the South, but now higher energy prices make it economical in most regions of the nation.

Solar heating and cooling systems exploit a neglected resource. Solar heating has already caught the public's eye through widespread publicity of the relatively few solar homes built around the country. The sun's energy is gathered in rooftop collectors to provide most of the energy for heating. Additional research and development is expected to produce air conditioning systems which use this solar heat, further expanding the usefulness and benefits of this approach. Under a Project grant,[5] the California Institute of Technology's Environmental Quality Laboratory has studied the many institutional and technical problems which must be overcome before solar space heating and cooling can play a major role in the U.S. energy economy. Because of the difficulties and higher costs associated with installing solar heating and cooling in existing homes, the Project estimates that this technology will achieve widespread use in new homes only after 1985.

Industrial heat production accounted for 28 percent of total energy consumption in 1968 and it offers a major opportunity for conservation. Improvements involve both existing and new technology. Heat recovery systems which use the heat from the exhaust gases of a furnace or other processes to warm incoming air have been around for years, but with cheap energy it was not often economically attractive to install them. The economics are now more favorable.

A similar approach combines process steam generation (60 percent of industrial heat production) with electric production. Whenever fossil or nuclear fuels are used to generate electric power, about two-thirds of the heat is released into the environment. Sometimes this waste heat can be used to generate process steam or heat. When this concept is used in residential or commercial applications, it is called "total energy." It is also used in industrial applications where high temperature energy is used to generate electric power before it is used as process steam. The hardware—whether it be diesel engines, gas turbines or steam turbines—exists and is becoming a better investment as energy prices rise. Institutional and technical problems associated with operating these systems as part of a larger electric power system need to be solved before they will achieve more widespread use.

The heat pump principle may also be used to produce process steam. A Thermo Electron study[6] for the Project has focused on this and other industrial energy applications. Residential heat pumps can frequently use the outdoor air as a source of low grade energy. However, the surrounding air may not contain enough heat for producing industrial steam. Industrial or power plant waste heat, low-temperature, solar-flat-plate collectors or ground water could fill this need. This approach is still in the research stage, but looks promising.

The use of energy in automobiles is also a significant fraction of the nation's energy budget and offers technical options for conservation. Overall vehicle weight and fuel consumption are closely related as discussed in Section 1. The current trend toward smaller vehicles will produce energy savings. Technical developments—for example, the use of radial tires, better streamlining, and improved matching of the engine, transmission and differential—could improve gasoline mileage without reducing the size or versatility of the automobile. Such improvements would result from design changes using existing technology. More fundamental changes such as the use of the diesel engine or electric propulsion systems to replace the internal combustion engine could also reduce the energy required for automobile transportation but would take longer to implement.

The major uncertainties in this scenario are political, institutional and economic questions rather than physical or technical limitations. A few of the technical fixes such as solar heating and cooling, the use of heat pumps to produce industrial steam, and alternatives to the internal combustion engine require some more R&D, but most of them are available commercially today. A fundamental assumption in this scenario is that individual and corporate consumers of energy would in fact respond to higher prices and direct federal action, and use these more efficient technologies.

Policies to Implement Conservation Measures

The basic tool for achieving the energy savings in the *technical fix* scenario is a market place in which energy is priced to reflect its full costs to society. At this point in our study, it is not clear just what the price level of energy would be with all existing subsidies removed, and the total social or environmental costs included in the price. Nor has the impact of higher prices on the level of demand been established with any degree of certainty. It appears, however, that market prices alone will not bring about all of the energy savings possible. Government policy changes are needed in order to eliminate institutional obstacles so that the market place can function more effectively. Other changes may be necessary to encourage market decisions in favor of conservation rather than consumption. Finally, in those instances in which market solutions are not feasible, direct regulation may be required. Any tax or regulation measures, of course, run the risk of distorting rather than correcting the market, and the social and economic consequences of government action should be weighed against the benefits.

Improving the operation of the market system requires that consumers have better information about the energy performance of the items they buy in terms of Btu's and dollars. The most immediate need appears to be for a "Truth in Energy Law" to require labeling for automobiles, appliances and even homes which clearly spells out average energy use and operating costs. The object is to give a purchaser the opportunity of making an informed decision on the basis of both the initial cost and the fuel costs for running the item over time. Today the consumer often lacks the information to take energy operating costs into account.

Information is useful only when the purchaser has a real choice of products and access to the credit needed to finance capital investments. Many government and private actions are needed to overcome this problem. One exemplary approach to financing additional insulation in private homes has already been initiated by a few utilities.[7] The company provides homeowners with low-interest loans, repayable through their utility bills, to meet insulating costs. The gas costs are, of course, reduced due to the lowered fuel heating requirements. This reduction is usually more than enough to offset the cost of insulation within a year, providing a vivid example of the benefits of life cycle costing.

In many instances, however, it will take more than better information to correct existing imbalances in the market or to shift the balance in favor of conservation. Taxes and subsidies are the basic tools for dealing with this, as discussed in Section 2. Metals recycling is a case in point. Depletion allowances on raw materials and regulated freight rates currently favor the use of new metals. Unless there are significant technical breakthroughs which would make processing waste metals much cheaper than at present, specific government action will be needed to encourage recycling. Removal of the subsidies on new metals, or the provision of comparable ones for scrap, as well as federally-funded demonstration of recycling metals from urban wastes, might be required.

In the transportation sector, a similar strategy of removing subsidies for less energy-efficient modes of transportation, and of supporting urban mass transportation and intercity railroads with new federal funding, would be necessary to achieve the savings projected in this scenario. Highway and air transportation now receive most of the government support in the transportation sector.

Federal research and development (R&D) funding is a common method for subsidizing civilian activities. It is being used extensively for developing energy supply, but to a much lesser degree for energy consumption technology. Basic R&D on energy conservation in building construction, equipment design and industrial processing could provide significant benefits to the public, but it may not be possible for an individual firm to profit from them and justify a corporate effort. Joint government-industry demonstration projects could pay large dividends if they were designed to encourage widespread implementation of the technology rather than simple technical development.

Some areas of the economy, particularly the industrial sector, are too varied and complex to address with specific taxes and subsidies. Here the use of a broadly based excise tax which reflects the social costs of using energy may be an effective tool. Such a tax could produce moderately higher prices sufficient to stimulate the use of less energy-intensive industrial processes.

Other areas of the economy such as the residential and transportation sectors may not be as amenable to market oriented solutions. Where additional information is not enough to stimulate the changes, and taxes or subsidies cause undesirable equity problems or do not work, regulatory measures may be used. Energy performance standards which specify the energy efficiency of buildings, appliances and automobiles have been suggested. To preserve the most design flexibility and room for innovation, it is preferable to regulate performance—the maximum permissible heat loss from a building or minimum fuel economy for an automobile—rather than to specify the technology for accomplishing it. These regulations can be made rigid, permitting no deviations, or more flexible through a steeply graduated tax. This mixed approach might be used for automobiles: no tax for efficient cars meeting a certain minimum standard coupled with high taxes for less efficient cars.

Impact of Conservation on Supply

The substantial reduction in energy consumption in the *technical fix* scenario gives us greater flexibility to select those energy supply options with minimum environmental, social, economic, and foreign policy costs. Because less energy would be required, less expensive sources may be developed, less land would need to be devoted to energy production and less pollution would result from its consumption. Another important difference between the scenarios involves capital investment. Greater investments in energy consumption systems such as mass transit would be required in the *technical fix* scenario, but there would be less investment in new energy supply facilities. A detailed evaluation of these effects has not yet been completed.

Numerous supply mixes for the *technical fix* scenario are possible and three have been examined by the Project. All of the cases move rapidly toward self-sufficiency. The "base case" achieves it first by developing all of the domestic sources. A domestic fossil fuel (or low nuclear) case requires oil, gas, and coal production approaching the *historical growth* scenario. A high nuclear case permits domestic oil, gas and coal production to level off after 1980. Each of these cases is depicted in Figure 13.

The "base case" demonstrates that a sustained effort to introduce energy-conserving technologies into the economy reduces the pressure upon energy suplies. For instance, domestic oil production needs to grow only about half as much by 1985 and 2000 as it would under the comparable *historical growth* supply case. The pace of Outer Continental Shelf and onshore Alaskan oil and gas development, as well as shale oil and coal synthetics development, could be much lower, and self-sufficiency could be achieved sooner. Domestic natural gas development would parallel the pattern set by domestic oil. Coal and nuclear power are also estimated to grow significantly above current levels in the "base case" but again less rapidly than in the *historical growth* scenario.

Expanding certain energy sources, even at the reduced rates possible in this scenario, is a source of increasing concern to individuals concerned with environmental degradation and regional impacts. The other two supply cases reflect the options of curtailing the development of one or more of the most controversial sources.

The low nuclear case assumes a political decision that the risks of nuclear power are too great to continue its growth as presently projected. Nuclear power could be limited to plants presently operating or under construction, pending resolution of the safety and environmental issues concerning nuclear power. Nuclear power could then be phased out, if these issues were not resolved. Due to the long lead time in constructing nuclear power plants it would be about 10 years before such a decision would affect electric power production or before new plants could be brought into production if it were rescinded. Phasing out nuclear power would greatly restrict future supply options.

Similarly, in the *technical fix* scenario, the nation could choose not to expand coal mining generally, in either the East or the West, because of environmental or social problems, or to restrict surface mining in particular. As shown in the high nuclear case in Figure 8, this action could be accommodated in the *technical fix* scenario. The amount of nuclear power required to fill the gap would be less than is required in the *historical growth* scenario.

Although not shown in Figure 13, a supply case which involves little or no increase in domestic oil and gas above current levels would be possible through a combination of nuclear and coal development. This case reflects a serious limitation on oil and gas resources or a decision not to develop the Atlantic and Pacific OCS. It would involve greater total energy consumption because more raw energy would be converted to electric power or synthetic liquids and gas with resultant energy conversion losses.

But under the *technical fix* scenario, it would be necessary to increase at least *one* major source of energy significantly above current production levels. This point is indicated with the supply options shown in Figure 13. More oil, whether it is imported oil, traditional domestic petroleum, or synthetic oil, is required in all but the high nuclear case. More natural gas and coal are included in all of the supply cases. Even nuclear power increases in all of the cases, although it is kept to a minimum in the low nuclear case. The size of these increases varies widely depending on the option selected. For coal the increases range from 30 percent to 300 percent and for nuclear the range is even larger. Due to their large current production,

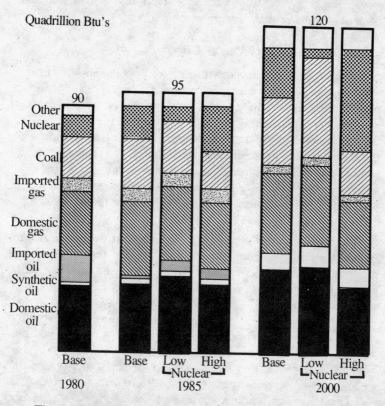

Figure 13. Energy Supply for the Technical Fix Scenario

the percentage increases in petroleum liquids and gas are not so large, except in terms of specific sources such as shale oil, coal liquids and oil from the Atlantic and Pacific Outer Continental shelves.

In the *historical growth* scenario, this flexibility in supply is *not* possible. Major sources like nuclear power or strip-mined coal cannot be eliminated, only developed at a slower rate.

Finally, since reduced growth in energy use gives a lower total energy use, new sources of energy such as solar or geothermal that may be environmentally or otherwise superior could contribute a greater fraction of the energy supply in a shorter period. The economy is also less dependent on short term payoffs from its energy research and development programs. A greater proportion of the federal R&D could be focused on long term energy sources such as solar energy, wind energy, and controlled thermonuclear fusion than would be possible with more rapid energy growth.

A Zero Energy Growth Scenario

The concept of zero growth, first for population, later for resource use and now for energy in particular, has caught the attention of many citizens.[8-13] This stems in part from a growing concern that we are rapidly approaching the limits to growth on our planet. Besides the concern over physical limits, there is growing dissatisfaction with the automatic acceptance of "progress," as well as a feeling of "dehumanization" that stems from disillusionment with ever-growing consumption of material goods, and with the huge bureaucracies which produce, dispense, regulate and otherwise service those goods.

One of the Project's scenarios for the future is designed to work out the implications of zero growth in energy. It is not our aim to explore the notion of zero economic growth. On the contrary, our preliminary work suggests that some sectors of the economy must grow vigorously for the nation to reach zero energy growth in a satisfactory way.

The transition to zero energy growth might come about naturally in response to ever-rising prices for energy and other commodities which result from scarcity or environmental limitations. It might also be one feature of the transition to a "post-industrial society,"[14] with an emphasis on services rather than goods production.

There are many reasons for seriously considering a *zero energy growth* (ZEG) option.

First, it is important to note that there is a fundamental difference between zero and slow growth. The slow growth of the *technical fix* scenario serves, in effect, to buy time before the problems associated with high consumption become acute. If the pace and mix of economic growth remains unchanged, energy consumption in the *technical fix* scenario would resume at a higher rate of growth, beyond the year 2000, as new opportunities for cutting out waste become harder to find. Even if the *technical fix* growth rate stays at 1.7 percent per year extended into the next century, a level of 180 quadrillion Btu's would be reached by 2025 and 275 quadrilion Btu's per year by 2050.

Providing the energy supplies to meet such demand levels would strain existing technology and known resources to the utmost. New technologies like nuclear fusion may be developed in time to support increasing energy growth early in the 21st century. But they are by no means certain to come to the rescue. They could prove to be less feasible or more polluting than they now appear.

Second, even if new technologies are developed, the earth has a finite capacity for absorbing environmental insults. What these finite limits are is uncertain. Recent scientific calculations indicate that the world may be rapidly approaching certain of those limits.[15] Continued rapid growth in the burning of fossil fuels for the next 30 years means an accompanying atmospheric buildup of carbon dioxide and particle matter. Analysis increasingly suggests that this could trigger substantial global climatic change.[16,17] A "point of no return" may be reached as soon as 30 years from now or as many as 100 or more years into the future. One prudent response to this uncertainty would be to plan now for reaching a manageable level of energy use as soon as possible.

A third reason for zero energy growth in the United States is simply that the rich nations of the world may limit their energy consumption either by choice or necessity so that the poor nations have a better opportunity, especially when it comes to using non-renewable resources, of achieving a decent standard of living.[13] Because of its influence in world affairs, America could take the lead in restraining its consumption of resources.

A fourth motivating factor for the *zero energy growth* scenario is the concern by some people that rapidly growing technology is dominating their lives and is beyond their control. There is a growing unwillingness among many citizens to leave to experts in remote bureaucracies the task of determining what technologies are or are not socially acceptable.

Both the *historical growth* and *technical fix* energy futures assume that there will be long term growth in the large industrial complexes which supply, process and use energy. Effective public participation in the decisions about the desirability of these large technologies has been virtually impossible. Events move too fast, technical knowledge is too specialized and the future becomes the present before we know it. For example, the social acceptability of nuclear power is only now being publicly debated, many decades and many billions of dollars later. With zero energy growth, the pace of development and innovation would be more amenable to public involvement. Gradual decentralization of technology could be an important element in the economic and institutional reorganization necessary to achieve a ZEG scenario.

The *zero energy growth* scenario we are developing closely parallels the *technical fix* scenario until the mid-1980's, and then reaches zero or even negative growth in the period thereafter. The nature of the economy in a zero energy growth society would certainly be very different from that of the other scenarios. But economic activity would not stagnate. Present-day society is geared to a relatively heedless use of plentiful, relatively low-cost energy. To develop a society that husbands its resources, including energy, would require a different kind of economic emphasis.

Redesign of cities and transportation systems would be a must. Growth in energy-intensive industries, like making plastics from petrochemicals, would be deemphasized. Instead there would be more vigorous growth in the service sector of the economy (education, medicine, government, etc.) and in industries which use less energy. The trend toward a service economy in the United States is already well under way, the service sector share of the labor force having increased from 50 to 60 percent during the last two decades. In the ZEG scenario, the shift would accelerate.

The idea of *zero energy growth* sometimes evokes the image of Spartan austerity. The ZEG future we envision does not match this image. An energy consumption level of 100 quadrillion Btu's per year in 2000 would provide 10 percent more energy per person than the United States uses today. And the energy would be used more efficiently, thus providing more benefits to society. There is nothing inherent in the ZEG scenario which would preclude national redistribution of the "energy income." Those who do not have an adequate standard of living need not be stopped from achieving one because of lack of energy. Nor is there any inherent reason why those in the middle to high energy income brackets would have to give up any of the things they enjoy today.

It would, however, mean an end to the "more is better" philosophy, replacing it with one saying "enough is best." There would be a saturation point where no further increases in annual energy consumption would be needed. Further, because of its greater efficiency in using energy, the ZEG scenario would include many more energy benefits than the nation now enjoys. All of the householder's basic energy needs could be met. Appliances like air conditioners and dishwashers, often classed as luxuries today, could be in such wide use as to be considered "basic." Use of electronic devices such as stereo high fidelity sound systems would be quite compatible with the scenario since they use little electricity.

Energy Characteristics of the ZEG Scenario

At this stage in our work we are still quantifying some of the important characteristics of a ZEG society. What we can do here is identify the areas where we believe the extra energy savings of the ZEG scenario may be found.

An important point to begin with is that structural changes in one sector of the energy economy often have profound effects in other sectors.

Transportation

For example, consider transportation. In the ZEG scenario, automotive energy requirements would be markedly reduced, not because cars would be still smaller or more efficient than those in the *technical fix* scenario, but because people would be spending less time traveling, especially in commuting. To save the time wasted in commuting, they would live closer to work or closer to schools and shopping areas. This kind of decision can be encouraged by governmental action. Present government policies, like income tax breaks to homeowners and FHA loans, encourage home ownership in the suburbs, and away from work in the central city. Government efforts to draw people back to central cities might involve such a simple but important "non-energy" policy as equalizing tax benefits for homeowners and renters.

Another approach to further reducing energy in transportation would be to design new communities where homes are close to jobs and commerce. In both the revitalized core city and the new community, people could readily get about within the community by foot, bicycle, or mass transit. Some new communities could be built as satellites to urban core cities, connected to the urban center and other satellites by rapid mass transit links. Another transportation feature of this scenario could be development of efficient rapid rail transport between urban centers up to four or five hundred miles apart. Air transportation would be used primarily for longer trips.

Residential Use

This "transportation strategy" for ZEG has several important implications for residential energy use. One of them is that the trend toward multi-family housing would be greater than in the other scenarios. This in turn means that energy requirements per household would drop. Our research shows that household energy consumption is much lower in multi-family than in single family dwellings. Another energy-saving opportunity comes with more multi-family units: greater potential use of on-site total energy systems, which generate electricity and use the waste heat for space conditioning.

Commercial Use

The commercial sector of the energy economy would probably involve more energy use in the ZEG than in the *technical fix* scenario, because more people would have jobs in the service sector, and energy is needed to support these jobs. But this would be more than offset by reductions in industrial energy use.

Industrial Use

There are several ways to reduce energy growth in industry. Sharply reduced growth in energy-intensive industries and more emphasis on agriculture, electronics and other high-technology, low-energy activities is vital. For example, the growth in energy-intensive industries might be exported to those parts of the world where energy is cheap—a trend that is already developing due to natural economic forces. The nation could import more of its fertilizer and aluminum, so long as it could pay for them through exports. We could, for example, extend our capacity to export farm products and high technology, two areas where we have a comparative advantage and where energy requirements are relatively low.

94

With slower growth in petrochemicals we could expect curtailed growth in the use of plastics, especially for purposes such as the packaging of food products.

It is possible to design industrial products so that they are easy to recycle. Automobiles themselves could be recycled, and so could their valuable, constituent materials, such as copper and aluminum. Performance standards might be developed that would require recyclability as a design feature of new products. Recycling not only saves the basic materials but greatly reduces the energy requirements for their manufacture. Greater stress on durability of many manufactured products could also be a major energy and materials saver.

Supply

Supplying the energy to meet a *zero energy growth* scenario has many fewer problems than supplying the other scenarios. In addition to reducing demands on the traditional resources, this scenario places emphasis on renewable resources such as solar power, wind energy and the conversion of agricultural and other wastes to energy. Simple, decentralized energy systems such as roof-top solar collectors and windmills could play a more significant role if consumption were not growing. We could redesign our agricultural systems so as to collect animal and plant wastes and use them as fuel. This new source of fuel would be a useful by-product of growth in farm output for export.

Achieving ZEG

This discussion has described some general features of our ZEG scenario as it is evolving in our thinking. Our analysis so far indicates that the implications of *zero energy growth* for our economic and political systems might be significant. Yet managing a transition to *zero energy growth* appears to be possible *if* the change takes place gradually over ten to twenty years as part of long term planning and a growing social consensus as to its desirability.

In order to achieve a smooth transition, policies which allow gradual increases in energy prices through energy excise taxes in addition to removal of existing subsidies would be needed. Government fiscal and monetary policies to maintain economic growth and full employment during this period would be crucial. Many of the policy tools now used to achieve this objective serve to increase energy-intensive capital investment. In a ZEG scenario full employment would require a different economic game plan. Special programs would be required to provide displaced workers with new jobs during the transition.

Some of these changes, such as zero population growth, are already beginning to take place without government action. There is no clear indication that more government coercion would be needed to achieve this scenario than the others.

Work is continuing on this scenario. In our final report, we expect to describe it in detail.

Summary

THE ENERGY PROBLEMS facing the nation stem from a long history of neglect and oversight; they will require time and a rigorous effort to overcome. No single villain brought us to this point and no simple action will get us out. But our diverse national resource base and the capability we possess for using energy more efficiently give us room to maneuver.

The gap between domestic energy consumption and domestic production emerged in the 1950s and has grown rapidly since 1970. In recent years imported oil has provided virtually all of our annual growth in energy. The gap grew not by design but through a hodgepodge of government, industry and consumer decisions, which were often unrelated to energy supply and demand calculations. These actions ranged from the passage of new national laws protecting the environment, to personal decisions to buy large air conditioned cars, to federal regulations which encouraged refinery construction abroad. They all contributed to the leveling off of domestic energy production and a simultaneous steady rise in consumption.

Extricating ourselves from this problem will take time. Increasing domestic supplies or implementing new, more efficient energy consumption technologies usually takes several years because of the large capital investments involved. Unless oil imports can be increased at an acceptable economic and political price, which is possible but not very probable, the only way to reduce the gap in the short term will be to restrict consumption. Making do with less fuel than we have grown accustomed to for heating and cooling buildings, driving automobiles or running industry will not be easy. Jobs, prices and our old ways of life may be compromised in the short term as we work to overcome the energy gap. The challenge for government in the short term is twofold: (1) to manage the shortage so that no individual or group bears an undue burden; and (2) to take short-term actions which do not significantly restrict options for the future.

This is critical, because in the medium and longer term, the picture is much brighter. We have outlined three descriptive scenarios of the future to show the range of feasible energy consumption patterns from which the nation can choose. These scenarios differ very markedly in their impacts on availability of energy supply, the environment, foreign policy, lifestyles, and the economy. One scenario is based on the persistence of present growth trends in energy production and consumption and stresses the policies needed to satisfy that growth in a socially acceptable manner; another is a "technical fix" solution, which maintains the same growth in energy services, but stresses policies needed to reduce growth in energy use through improved efficiency; as a third option, we consider a *zero energy growth* scenario which would require changes in both lifestyles and the economy to reach a steady no-growth state in energy consumption by the late 1980's. A comparative analysis of these scenarios, together with a detailed exploration of the policies needed to implement them, will be presented in the Project's final report.

Choices that we make today will profoundly affect our options for the future. Three policy areas stand out because they urgently require decisions whose consequences will be far-reaching. First, international policy is closely linked to energy policy; the challenge is to develop the two in concord. Environmental policy too is intertwined with energy since producing energy and using it always harms the environment to some extent. Federal energy resource management is a third area which has an essential bearing on energy issues. It affects adequacy of domestic energy supplies, energy prices, and environmental protection, because most of the nation's undeveloped energy resources are on government land and owned by the public.

What we wish to emphasize in this preliminary report of our work is that the nation does have energy choices. There is more than one path before us; each has its own advantages and pitfalls. Our first task as energy-conscious citizens is to inform ourselves of what lies ahead before we choose our way.

Advisory Board Comments

Statement by the Advisory Board

The Energy Policy Project's preliminary report is the first product of a comprehensive effort to define the problems and appraise the evidence concerning the United States' energy situation. It outlines an orderly framework within which the possible public choices can be assessed, and it notes major points at which basic information is available or lacking. Rather than offering solutions, it suggests lines along which public debate fruitfully should proceed.

As members of the Advisory Board for the Project, we warmly supported the Ford Foundation's initiation of this pioneer enterprise in late 1971. We have shared in critical review of the study design and of the proposed allocation of funds for subsidiary investigations. However, the final responsibility for the study plan, the choice of grantees, and the presentation of findings rests with the Project's director.

Considering that only a few of the reports by the grantees are in final form, and that the Director's analysis is in progress, we have mixed views as to the wisdom of issuing a preliminary report at this time. Some of us think it prudent to defer any publication until the entire investigation is finished. Others join in the director's judgment that this interim document will enhance policy discussion during a critical period and will provide a setting within which individual grantee reports may be appraised.

The advisory board is united in reserving detailed comment until all of the findings of the project are available. A few of us believe certain parts of the preliminary report require a note of dissent at this juncture, and those views follow in supplemental statements that have not been reviewed by the other members.

On the necessity of promptly deepening and refining the level of national appraisal of the U.S. energy future, we have no doubts. The issues are too complex to lend themselves to precipitous or piecemeal solutions. They are too urgent to permit further delay in soberly exploring possible alternative actions. While suspending judgments on specific conclusions we believe that the preliminary report will spur incisive public thinking about the elements of a genuine national energy policy.

Gilbert F. White, Chairman
Dean Abrahamson
Lee Botts
Harvey Brooks
Donald C. Burnham
John J. Deutsch
Joseph L. Fisher
John D. Harper
Philip S. Hughes
Minor S. Jameson
Carl Kaysen
Michael McCloskey
Norton Nelson
Alex Radin
Joseph R. Rensch
Charles R. Ross
Joseph Sax
Julius Stratton
William Tavoulareas
J. Harris Ward

Statement by D. C. Burnham, Chairman, Westinghouse Electric Corporation

I am concerned that this preliminary report makes it sound too easy to solve our energy problems and that it makes it seem that life styles would not change significantly with lower energy usage.

It is my belief that the following are major basic deficiencies in the report:

1. *Future Energy Demand is Underestimated.* The "Technical Fix Scenario" seriously underestimates the magnitude of future energy demand required to maintain a healthy economic situation in the United States. The very substantial energy reductions postulated in that scenario result from inadequately supported and unrealistic assumptions regarding projected efficiency improvements and acceptable life-style changes.

2. *Future Oil-Gas Production is Overestimated.* The report assumes that future U.S. petroleum and natural gas production can be greatly increased above current levels, thereby relieving the pressure for other energy sources for the remainder of the century. That assumption regarding increased oil and gas production is in direct opposition to studies by most government agencies and petroleum industry experts, who have concluded that the peak in U.S. oil and gas production has already passed, and that new areas such as Alaska and offshore Atlantic sites will merely retard the decline.

As a result of items #1 and #2, the report seriously understates the magnitude of the energy gap which must be closed by energy sources other than petroleum and natural gas. This understatement and overoptimism can mislead the nation to believe that we have adequate time and numerous options which in fact do not exist.

3. *The Finite Nature of Oil-Gas Resources is Ignored.* The report almost entirely overlooks the finite nature of petroleum and natural gas resources, and the fact that both U.S. and world resources will be virtually exhausted in a few decades.

By so doing, the report encourages continued and increased reliance on oil and gas, our smallest and most rapidly depleting energy resources. In no instance is an analysis made nor even a warning given of the potentially catastrophic consequence of following a policy of continued heavy reliance on petroleum and natural gas for the nation's future energy base.

I will reserve more detailed comments for the final report.

Comments of J. Harris Ward, Director, Commonwealth Edison Company
Nuclear Power

In a number of places the report suggests that nuclear power is an emerging science—risky and only partially understood. The impression is also given that its contribution to power production in this country and elsewhere in the world is insignificant. Roughly one-third of Chicago and northern Illinois' electricity is now made with nuclear energy, and the oldest atomic unit has been operating for almost 14 years. The state electric monopoly in France has decided that all new power stations will be nuclear. Twenty nations other than the U.S., including all major industrial powers, are moving ahead on the nuclear power front.

A proposal to defer nuclear development in this country is dangerous to the national security and the national welfare for a number of reasons. In the first place, nuclear power is one of the best means of solving our energy shortage and our environmental problems. Secondly, a nation which hesitates to keep up technologically today must make double or triple the effort to catch up tomorrow. Thirdly, nuclear power has a fine safety record. If it proves to have hazards which we are unable to manage, with existing methods, we can and must learn to handle the hazards with other methods—not abandon the technology. Finally, nuclear waste management methods are new but they are not beyond our knowledge or capacity. If they should turn out to be inadequate, they too can be corrected.

Nevertheless social activists and a small minority of scientists, representing what they consider to be the public interest, have succeeded in extending the construction time of most recent nuclear units on the basis of environmental and safety concerns. This report considers and almost suggests a moratorium on nuclear power development until disagreements among scientists have been settled. The cost of avoiding decision until scientists are unanimous will, in my judgment, place too great a burden on the American people.

Zero Energy Growth

ZEG, zero energy growth, is discussed in some detail in the preliminary report. ZEG may reduce energy problems somewhat but its long-term social, economic, and international effects will be both massive and unpredictable.

The rising standard of living in the world and in the U.S. is related very directly to the substitution of other forms of energy for human sweat. Progress in this respect has increased geometrically as the ox and the mule have been replaced by wood, coal, oil, gas, and uranium in an ever-increasing supply of energy units. Fission is here and fusion is on the way. Neither the minds nor the data are available today to tell us the effects of additions to or changes in the energy mix, nor the growth rate of total energy use.

Statement by John D. Harper, Chairman, Aluminum Company of America

I have been able to endorse the general statement made by the Advisory Board, but feel that it is necessary to append my positions on the two points stated below:

(1) On page 14 and page 15 of this interim statement suggestions are put forth to establish a centralized government energy data bank, and a little later on to require disclosure of development proposals. While I am sympathetic with the principle that governmental policies must not be made in an information vacuum, I feel constrained to raise a point of caution with respect to these suggestions lest they lead to further government interference with the efficient operation of our competitive private enterprise system. I believe that increasing concentration of power in the Federal Government is an ever-developing danger to our economic and political freedoms.

(2) On page 32 the statement pertaining to the establishment of a government corporation to explore and develop federally controlled resource areas is completely anathema. This point is first raised on page 14 in the section titled *Public Ownership and Resource Development.* I can think of no single approach to the solutions of our current and future energy and resource problems that would prove as counter productive as this suggestion. If we have learned anything from the past concerning government intervention in the private sector, it is that governmental operation of industrial activities has proved an abysmal failure in virtually every case.

Comments by W. P. Tavoulareas, President, Mobil Oil Corporation

The Energy Policy Project was established by the Ford Foundation in May, 1972, with the purpose expressed at that time as that of "shedding light on the total energy problem . . . to help prepare an informed and reasoned base for a national energy policy."

The preliminary report cannot be expected to provide the full answer which a final report hopefully would. It may therefore appear to be unfair to comment on this report, recognizing that much work remains to be done. We agree with the other members of the Advisory Board that detailed comments should await the final report. However, the interim report deals with many important issues that are being sharply debated before the public at the present time. Many of these issues involve the oil industry. The alternatives examined by the report make express or implied judgments with respect to the oil industry that will necessarily receive a good deal of public attention. Indeed, the major impact of the Project on the oil industry may occur before a final report is issued. Since I am the only member of the Advisory Board from an operating oil company, it seemed not only desirable but necessary for me to make some comments at this time, despite my reluctance to prejudge the final results of the study some months hence.

It seems to me that the clear implication of the report is that we should delay the development of additional energy supplies on the assumption that they will not be needed because we can reduce our use of energy. The alternative is, of course, to accelerate the development of supplies while we examine the various possibilities for reducing consumption to see whether such reductions are consistent with the way of life we want and with expectations for improving the way of life of many poorer members of our society.

Recognizing the uncertainties that always exist in attempts to understand the future, especially in a subject that reaches into so many aspects of society, the Project has constructed three alternative energy consumption case studies (scenarios). It is important to understand the implications of the rather complex data which formed the basis for the three scenarios. Although the report avoids making specific recommendations, it is clear that there is little enthusiasm for the "historical growth" scenario. The scenario involving lower levels of growth is called the "technical fix." The report makes the point that the technical fix scenario "still provides a quality of life . . . that, to our minds, at least, differs little from the historical growth scenario." It is virtually impossible for the reader to reach a judgment as to whether or not this is true, based on information given in the report. It is therefore important to see what is meant by the "historical growth" scenario, in relation to present living conditions in the United States, and then to see how "technical fix" involves further changes.

"Historical growth" is described simply as continuation of the rate of growth that prevailed in the period 1950 through 1972—3.4%

per year. Elsewhere in the report it is acknowledged that energy consumption has in fact accelerated in the last half of the period just mentioned. Unfortunately, the only history from which consumption in the 1980's can be judged is the pattern which has been more recently established in the latter half of the 60's and thus far in the 70's. Indeed, forecasts of energy consumption which were prepared by others before the current crisis generally reflected higher consumption levels. As the report indicates, the current consumption growth rates are running a full percentage point higher than in the 50's and early 60's. While such a difference sounds small, the continuation of the current trends through 1985 would produce a very much higher consumption level than contemplated in the "historical growth" scenario. The differences are significant.

If we look at the year 1985 we see that the "historical growth" scenario has a 5.4 quadrillion BTU's lower level of residential and commercial energy consumption than results from extending current trends. This is equivalent to the current space heating requirements of the 25 million households in the states of the East coast, together with that of their related shopping and business areas. In industrial and raw materials usage, the variance by which the historical growth case falls below current trends is equivalent to the combined usage of the paper, printing, and furniture industries, which together employ more than 2 million workers. In transportation, the difference is equivalent to more than the fuel requirements of ten million vehicles. Thus, the so-called historical growth scenario is in no sense a reflection of current trends, but in fact involves a sharp reduction from recent historical growth.

Further reductions associated with the technical fix scenario are also of a very major nature. These reductions amount to a further 19 quadrillion BTU's. To give some perspective to the size of that number, it should be noted that if the reduction in U.S. imports resulting from the oil embargo is taken at about 2 million barrels per day, that reduction is equivalent to 4.2 quadrillion BTU's. Consequently, the technical fix scenario reduces demand by the amount we have just discussed for the "historical growth" scenario, *plus* a further amount equivalent to more than *four* Arab embargoes. (Quite apart from the lifestyle implications of the substantial reductions in both scenarios, the report also implies that energy not used in one sector can be readily applied to another. In the relatively short period of time we are dealing with, this assumption is, at best, questionable.) It is therefore little wonder that the report notes that consumer education alone may not be sufficient to reduce consumption levels to the point contemplated in the technical fix scenario, that is, direct governmental controls would be required.

The report is not explicit in terms of all of the governmental controls that would be necessary to achieve such a major reduction in consumption, but some are implied. A few examples are the following:

- Utility rates should not be based upon the cost of service but instead should increase according to the size of the customer's requirements. The idea, of course, is to "discourage" industry from using energy (on the apparent assumption that the cost of the energy in industrial products is not passed on to customers).
- Taxes are mentioned at various points as a means of reducing usage of energy below the level determined by the forces of the marketplace.
- There is reference to "performance standards," which apparently means that a customer should not be permitted to purchase an energy-consuming appliance if the government feels it does not meet "performance standards."
- There is reference to the possibility of "encouraging" multi-family housing rather than than single-family housing.
- The use of automobiles and airplanes would be "discouraged."

Implicit in the report is the assumption that we will deal with the problems of the poor in a way that will not increase their energy consumption. Because of the wide disparity in standard of living in the United States, bringing the lower one-third of the population up to the average will require very large additional consumption of energy in the form of energy-using appliances and products. The only alternative method for improving standards of living for this sector is through some sort of redistribution among the population. Indeed, such a redistribution may be implied in the report. If automobiles, airplanes and single-family housing are to be restricted by the government, we will ultimately be allocating these "luxuries" across the population on some basis that is not made clear.

Even beyond the suggestion for a multiplicity of controls, the report also stresses alternatives which require detailed government planning. While there is a legitimate role for government in many aspects of our social and economic system, we must question whether making the government the operator of a commercial activity will produce an efficient result. The experience of the last few months with price controls and various allocation schemes points up the weakness of such a government role. We continue to believe that the market-place under a freely competitive system is the most efficient means of allocating resources. A businessman with a profit motive has the incentive to reduce costs. The oil industry has a record it need not be ashamed of in providing energy at low cost. For example, in the period 1967–1973 the price of gasoline increased less than 19%, while all consumer prices increased more than 33%. Thus, in terms of buying power of the 1967 dollar, the price of gasoline actually declined. It was only when the government regulations—much of it well intentioned —began to impact on the industry that it had difficulty in making available the necessary supplies.

No one today would seriously suggest a return to laissez-faire. Indeed, the oil industry was already subject to a network of controls, even before the current crisis. But during the last several years increased controls have progressively worsened the energy supply situation.

- In 1959 the mandatory import program was installed; modifications up through 1972 progressively discouraged the growth of U.S. refining capacity.
- The pipeline from the North Slope of Alaska was treated as a political football for more than five years while the industry marked time waiting for approval. (There are still hundreds of permits to be issued on the line.) This delay has also brought exploration in Alaska to a virtual standstill.
- The virtual government moratorium on federal offshore leasing from 1969 through 1972 sharply reduced the amount of acreage available for exploration in the United States.
- The suspension of operations on the leases in the Santa Barbara channel prevented exploration of leases that had already been purchased, and prevented the full development of discoveries already made. Some of the known reserves in that area are still not on production.
- The regulation of natural gas at a price lower than its heating value created enormous demand for the use of this fuel, while at the same time reducing the incentive to search for new gas supplies.
- The telescoping of the timetable for achieving low automotive emission levels effectively required the manufacture of automo-

biles with low efficiency, rather than permitting the orderly development of technology which would retain efficiency and meet the emission requirements at the same time.

Without these governmental restrictions there would have been no U.S. supply shortage in 1974.

There are also points of factual distortion in the report, two of which are the following:

• The reference to "windfall" profits of the oil industry is made without a corresponding recognition that these profits are only 2c per gallon or less and therefore are a minor component of increasing energy costs.

• The report is particularly unsound where it deals with the foreign tax credit. (Repeating inaccurate statements made by others does not make them true!) In point of fact, the tax credit does not permit the American companies operating abroad to pay any less income tax to the United States than they would if they had no foreign operations. Thus, the nub of the controversy on the tax credit comes down to the question as to whether U.S. companies should operate abroad, not whether they enjoy a reduction of their U.S. taxes by reason of such operations. We continue to believe that the U.S. has benefited from the foreign operations of the U.S. oil industry through enormous dividend remittances and through the import of the oil itself. To argue that these operations should lose foreign tax credit means in effect that they will be lost to foreign competitors; this is, in our mind, a curious position at the very time when the United States needs to import large amounts of foreign crude oil.

• The report implies that the foreign tax credit created an incentive for the oil companies to explore overseas rather than in the United States. The actual reason for foreign exploration overseas is very simple: First, the oil potential overseas was very great— since World War II oil industry foreign discoveries amounted to more than 10 times total U.S. reserves. Secondly, there was at the same time limited acreage available for exploration in the United States, as we have already indicated above. Finally, if a company were to choose between the foreign area and the U.S. *solely* on the basis of the amount of taxes paid in a given exploration venture, the clear choice would have to favor the U.S., since total taxes paid on a foreign operation would be equal or greater in every case.

There is considerable emphasis in the report on public participation in decisions to locate new energy facilities. We would like to suggest an additional element of public participation. The public should have the right to judge—through the mechanism of the marketplace—whether additional energy supplies are desirable or not. The judgment, of course, should be based upon the full cost (including environmental costs) of the additional supplies; and these costs should not be arbitrarily reduced so as to create a fictitious appearance of a cheap product. We believe strongly that the U.S. is suffering from an energy supply problem. We agree that waste of energy should be eliminated; but even when wastage is taken out of the system, the average consumer in this growing economy will continue to need more energy tomorrow than he does today.

The energy resources of the earth are virtually unlimited if one includes geothermal, nuclear, solar, wind and tidal energy, etc. As for oil, the potential there is also still very large. For example, we have not really begun to explore the continental margins. In just one such area, the North Sea, it is evident that Norway and the United Kingdom—both substantial importers of energy—will become self-sufficient within a few years. The same possibility exists for a number of other nations, with obvious implications for the world oil supply. Decisions to limit our future use of energy must therefore involve considerations other than ultimate supply.

We firmly believe the safest course for the U.S. will be to encourage the development of additional energy supplies while continuing the national dialogue with respect to the desirable level of consumption—whether it be "historical growth" or otherwise. In all likelihood the correct answer will not be as simple as any of the scenarios suggested; a mixed strategy will most likely be called for. We would like to suggest some elements of such a strategy.

• First, we should have the objective to eliminate government controls which interfere with the development of additional supplies.

• Secondly, we should go forward with the orderly development of supplies, even to the point of creating an energy surplus again. If it appears desirable the entire development scheme can later be modified at any stage in its implementation. We should recognize that all the decisions will not be taken at one time. Coal mines will be opened one at a time. Oil wells offshore will be drilled one at a time. Refineries will be built one at a time.

- Thirdly, the timetable on environmental objectives should be carefully reviewed in relation to the energy needs. Here we particularly emphasize we are referring to the *timetable* and not to the *objectives* themselves. We continue to believe that the advance of technology and the development of clean energy sources will permit us to realize our environmental objectives. We only ask that the two programs be viewed as part of a single problem, allowing for the tradeoffs between them.

- Fourthly, we must encourage energy research so that the problems that we have experienced in the 70's will not again become problems in the 80's and 90's. Energy resources are abundant; and if we have the technology to utilize them in an optimal fashion, we need have no concern for future energy growth.

- Finally, we must deal with the social costs of higher-priced energy. The appearance of higher energy costs in the economy will create dislocations. The extent of these dislocations is at present unclear. However, to the extent that there is an adverse impact on the lower income segments of the economy, we must deal with that problem and not turn our backs on it. To deal directly with (e.g., by subsidy) rather than through a general distortion of price levels in the economy, will in the end be the most effective and least expensive solution. Arbitrary controls which delay the development of additional supplies only aggravate the problem of the poor.

This solution to the energy problem would involve less controls than the report implies; would involve a return to a surplus of energy as a means of keeping prices down; would involve reasonable preservation of our environmental objectives; and would involve explicit attention to the problems of the poor.

In summary:

- The "historical growth" scenario reduces energy growth substantially below current levels; the technical fix scenario involves further very drastic reductions. The statement that the technical fix scenario involves no significant change in lifestyle is a conclusion, not a factual statement; it is not based upon detailed examination of the energy consumption changes which would be required.

- While no one denies the need for government planning and intervention in business affairs, the pervasive regulatory framework implicit in the report would involve government even more deeply than today in areas where it has been a notable failure: in directing the search for new energy supplies at reasonable cost to the consumer.

There are essentially two alternatives in dealing with the energy problem. The first would delay the development of new supplies *on the assumption* that energy usage can easily be reduced enough to bring supply and demand into balance. This is the case which the report implicitly adopts. The second alternative, not covered in the report, would increase supplies, eliminate waste usage, and examine aH implications of further energy reductions which may have an impact on lifestyles. We should ask ourselves which course carries the greater risk. If the assumptions behind the low growth cases are wrong the result will be energy scarcity, high energy prices, unemployment, and other economic and social dislocations. On the other hand, if the assumptions supporting the case for increased supplies are wrong we will have energy surplus and low prices. It seems clear to us that this latter risk is the more tolerable one.

Appendixes

Appendix A
Professional Staff, Consultants and Advisory Board

S. David Freeman, Director—former Head, Energy Policy Staff, Office of Science and Technology, Executive Office of the President

Monte Canfield, Jr, Deputy Director—former Chief, Division of Minerals, Bureau of Land Management, Department of the Interior

Pamela L. Baldwin, Project Assistant—formerly with Environmental Law Institute

Steven C. Carhart, Specialist—Technology Assessment—Social Application of Technology, Massachusetts Institute of Technology

John Davidson, Physicist—University of Michigan

Joy C. Dunkerley, Economist—formerly with Twentieth Century Fund

Charles Eddy, Project Counsel—formerly with Department of the Interior and Natural Resources Defense Council

Katherine B. Gillman, Writer—former newspaper correspondent and economic research assistant

Shelley Prosser, Librarian—MLS, University of Maryland

Lucille Larkin, Director of Public Information—former radio-TV correspondent and freelance reporter

Arjun B. Makhijani, Engineer—University of California, Berkeley

Francisco X. Otero, Economist—George Washington University.

Kenneth J. Saulter, Economist—University of California, Santa Barbara

Majester L. Seals, Project Assistant—formerly with Bureau of Land Management, Department of the Interior

David Sheridan, Editor—former Assistant Editor and Correspondent, LIFE

J. Frederick Weinhold, Senior Engineer—formerly with Office of Science and Technology, Executive Office of the President

Robert H. Williams, Physicist—Department of Physics and Institute for Environmental Quality, University of Michigan

Former Professional Staff

Michael Fortune	Jeremy Main
Mark Levine	Judith Pigossi
Patricia Lynch	Adam Sieminski

Support Staff

Evelyn Chisholm	
Shirley Cox	Sharon Lynn
Norma Dosky	Valerie Moore
Dieu Granados	Billie Truesdell

Former Support Staff

Annette Burke	
Cheryl Garner	Larry Dickter
Annette Kornblum	Rebecca Jacobsen
Patricia Pierson	Judith Miller

Consultants

Saud Al-Sowayel, Independent Consultant

James P. Beirne, Independent Consultant

Daniel Bell, Department of Sociology, Harvard University

Manson Benedict, Department of Nuclear Engineering Massachusetts Institute of Technology

Kenneth E. Boulding, Department of Economics, University of Colorado

Harrison Brown, Division of the Humanities and Social Science, California Institute of Technology

Ronald Brown, Washington Bureau, National Urban League

Barry Commoner, Center for the Biology of Natural Systems, Washington University

Rene Dubos, The Rockefeller University

John C. Esposito, Lawyer and Freelance Writer

Frances E. Francis, Economist and Lawyer

Irene Gordon, Freelance Researcher and Writer

Perry R. Hagenstein, New England Natural Resources Center

Hendrik S. Houthakker, Department of Economics, Harvard University

William Iulo, Department of Economics, Washington State University*

Walter J. Mead, Department of Economics, University of California, Santa Barbara*

---

* Full-time staff members for 1972–73 academic year.

113

Appendix B:
Major Research Studies for the Energy Policy Project

There follows a very brief description of the major research studies which the Energy Policy Project has commissioned from independent scholars and groups. Many of these studies are being published in the Project's multi-volume series of special reports (Ballinger Publishing Company, Cambridge, Massachusetts).

Subject of Study	Brief Description	Research Group	Research Director
Energy & Lifestyles	How energy use varies according to economic level and lifestyle.	Washington Center for Metropolitan Studies	Dr. Dorothy K. Newman, Senior Associate
Reclamation of Surface-Mined Land	Can Western coal be mined, and the land be reclaimed after mining?	National Academy of Sciences	Dr. Thadis W. Box, Utah State University
Nuclear Theft: Risks and Safeguards	Assesses the risk that nuclear materials may be stolen from the nuclear power industry to be used as weapons; safeguard measures.	International Research and Technology Corporation	Mason Willrich, University of Virginia Law School; Theodore B. Taylor, IR&T.
General Health Hazards of Energy Systems	The health hazards at various stages of producing and using energy.	American Public Health Association	Dr. Bertram W. Carnow, University of Illinois School of Medicine

116

Energy Costs of Pollution Control	How much energy is needed to clean up the environment?	University of Michigan	Marc Ross, Professor of Physics
Energy Content of Consumer Products	Analyses of pairs of similar products, to determine which requires more energy.	University of Illinois, Center for Advanced Computation	Bruce Hannon, Director, Energy Research Group
Energy Consumption in Manufacturing	How energy is used in six energy-intensive industries, and how energy might be saved by more efficient use.	The Conference Board	John G. Myers, Director of General Economics Research
Potential for Fuel Conservation in Industry	New technologies to improve energy efficiency in both energy-intensive industries and industries generally.	Thermo Electron Corporation	Lazarus Lazarides

117

Subject of Study	Brief Description	Research Group	Research Director
Urban Transportation and Energy Saving	Energy implications of several transportation alternatives.	Princeton University	Margaret Fels, Research Associate
Community Energy Systems, Institutional Problems	Non-technical barriers to innovation in residential energy systems; policy changes to promote innovation.	California Institute of Technology	Lester Lees, Director, Environmental Quality Laboratory
Energy and Architectural Design	Energy-saving potential in building design.	American Institute of Architects Research Corporation	John Eberhard, President, AIA Research Corporation
Institutional Framework for Energy Research and Development	How energy technology has been developed in the past; proposed changes for more effective R&D in the future.	Massachusetts Institute of Techology	J. Herbert Hollomon, Center for Policy Alternatives

Topic	Description	Investigator	Organization
Competition in the Energy Industry	Is the energy industry sufficiently competitive to protect the public interest in adequate supplies at reasonable prices?	Dr. Thomas Duchesneau, University of Maine	
Capital Flow and Profits	Projected capital requirements and profits in each sector of the energy industry.	Jerome Hass, Cornell University	
Utility Systems			
Institutional Structure	Legal and economic aspects of the regulated energy industries.	Dr. Charles Cicchetti, University of Wisconsin; Edward Berlin, Esq.	Public Interest Economics Center
Technology	Planning and operation of interregional electric power connections.	R. J. Ringlee, Project Leader	Power Technologies, Inc.

Subject of Study	Brief Description	Research Group	Research Director
Energy Prices	Past and current energy prices, by regions and by major consumer product: basic data.	Foster Associates, Inc.	Radford L. Schantz, Vice President
Taxes and Subsidies	The present system of energy taxes and subsidies, in relation to policy goals; possible new uses of taxes and subsidies to meet future energy policy goals.		Gerard M. Brannon, Georgetown University
Energy and Foreign Policy	U. S. energy policy and international relations; foreign policy and import options.	The Brookings Institution	Joseph Yager
The Federal Government and Energy	Energy policy decision-making in the federal government.	Natural Resources Defense Council	Thomas B. Stoel, Jr.; Edward L. Strobehn, Jr
Industry Outlook on Energy	The views of energy industry leaders on energy problems and goals.		John E. Gray

Energy Supply for the Future	Alternative sources of energy supply for the future, assuming energy growth at current rates.	Resources For the Future, Inc.	Sam Schurr, Director, Energy and Mineral Resources Division
Energy Forecasting: An Economic Integrating Model	An empirical model of the energy sector of the economy, to assist in forecasting future developments and analyzing policy options.	Data Resources, Inc.	Hendrik S. Houthakker; Dale W. Jorgenson
Data to supplement the integrating model, on intersectional flows of fuels and electrical energy; interindustry flows.		Jack Faucett Associates	John M. Rodgers, Senior Economist

Appendix C:

Charts and Tables

The next several pages bring together a few of the well known but scattered figures and facts about where energy comes from and how it is used, both for the United States and for the world.

Charts
1. Energy Consumption in the U.S., by Sources, Selected Years, 1880–1973
2. Sources of U.S. Energy Supply, 1920, 1950, 1973
3. End Uses of Energy, United States, 1968
4. U.S. Energy Production and Consumption, 1947–1973
5. Sources of World Energy Supply, 1950 and 1968
6. Energy Use per Capita, United States and World

Tables
1. Per Capita Energy Consumption, United States and World, Selected Years, 1920–1973
2. Major Energy Resources, United States
3. Major Energy Resources, World
4. U.S. Production and Consumption of Energy, Selected Years, 1950–1973
5. Federal Energy R&D Funding, Fiscal Year 1969 through Fiscal Year 1975
6. World Petroleum Production and Reserves, 1973

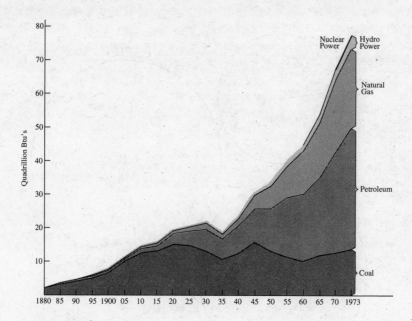

Chart 1. Energy Consumption in the U.S. by Sources, Selected Years 1880–1973

Notes: Energy includes fossil fuels and primary electricity; excludes wood. Petroleum includes natural gas liquids.
Source: U.S. Bureau of Mines

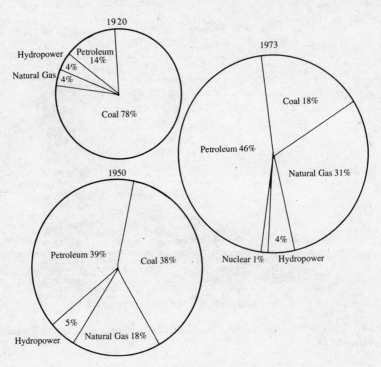

Chart 2. Sources of U.S. Energy Supply 1920, 1950, 1973

Source: U.S. Bureau of Mines

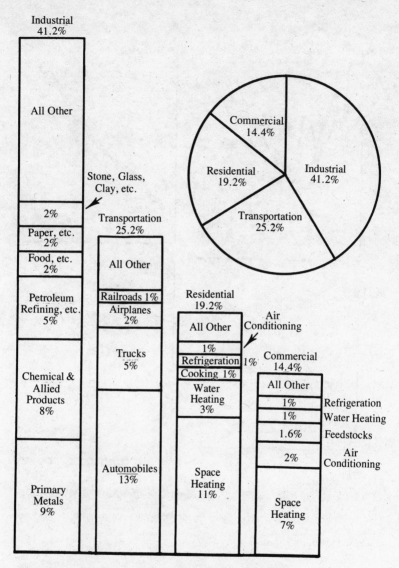

Chart 3. End Uses of Energy, United States, 1968

Source: Stanford Research Institute, "Patterns of Energy Consumption in U.S."

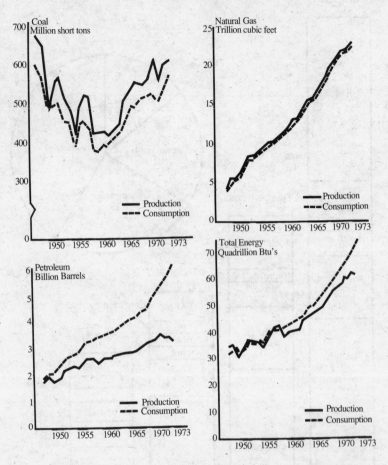

Chart 4. U.S. Energy Production and Consumption, 1947–1973

Notes: Natural gas production includes liquids. Petroleum consumption includes natural gas liquids
Source: U.S. Bureau of Mines

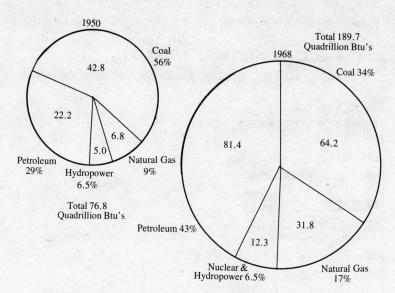

Chart 5. Sources of World Energy Supply, 1950 and 1968

Source: Sam Schurr ed., *Energy, Economic Growth and the Environment*

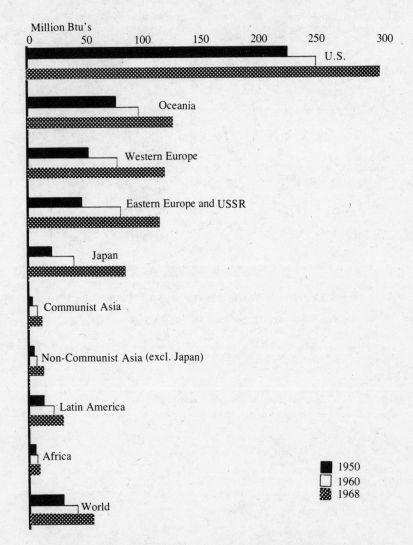

Million Btu's

| 0 | 50 | 100 | 150 | 200 | 250 | 300 |

U.S.

Oceania

Western Europe

Eastern Europe and USSR

Japan

Communist Asia

Non-Communist Asia (excl. Japan)

Latin America

Africa

World

■ 1950
□ 1960
▨ 1968

Chart 6. Energy Use Per Capita, U.S. and the World

Source: Sam Schurr ed., *Energy, Economic Growth and the Environment*

Table 1. Per Capita Energy Consumption, U.S. and World, Selected Years, 1920–1973

Year	Total U.S. (Trillion Btu)	Per Capita U.S. (Million Btu)	Total World (Trillion Btu)	Per Capita World (Million Btu)
1920	19,768	185.7		
1925	20,879	180.2	44,249	23.4
1930	22,253	180.6		
1940	23,877	180.1		
1950	33,992	223.2	76,823	30.7
1955	39,703	239.3	99,658	36.6
1960	44,569	246.7	124,046	41.5
1965	53,343	274.5	160,722	49.0
1967	58,265	293.2		
1968	61,763	307.7	189,737	54.5
1969	64,979	320.6		
1970	67,143	327.7		
1971	68,698	331.8		
1972	72,108	345.3		
1973	75,561	359.1		

Notes: "Energy" includes the commercial fossil fuels and primary electricity: firewood, animal wastes and most other non-commercial fuels are excluded from these figures. "World" includes the United States.

Sources: Joel Darmstadter, "Appendix," in Sam H. Schurr, ed., *Energy, Economic Growth, and the Environment,* Johns Hopkins Press, Baltimore, 1972, for figures on world consumption and population. U.S. Bureau of the Census, and U.S. Bureau of Mines for U.S. figures.

Table 2. Major Energy Resources, U.S.

	1973 Consumption (Quadrillion Btu)	Cumulative Production (Q Btu)	Reserves (Q Btu)	Recoverable Resources (Q Btu)	Remaining Resource Base (Q Btu)
Petroleum	34.7	605	302	2,910	16,790
Shale Oil	—	—	(465)	N/A	975,000
Tar Sands	—	—		N/A	168
Natural Gas	23.6	405	300	2,470	6,800
Coal	13.5	810	4,110	14,600	64,000
Strippable coal	N/A	N/A	925	2,600	2,600
Low-sulfur coal	N/A	N/A	2,390	N/A	38,200
Uranium					
Used in light-water reactors	.85	2	228	600	3,200
Used in breeders		—	17,700	47,000	200,000,000
Thorium used in breeders	—	—	4,200	17,500	570,000
Hydropower	2.9			5.8*	

Note: The terms "Reserves," "Recoverable Resources," and "Remaining Resource Base" are geological estimates. "Reserve" estimates are based on detailed geologic evidence, usually obtained through drilling, while the other estimates reflect less detailed knowledge and more geologic inference. All of these estimates are based on assumptions about technology and economics. They may increase over time as technology improves or prices increase.

N/A—not available
* ultimate capability

Table 3. Major Energy Resources, World

	Cumulative Production (Q Btu)	Reserves (Q Btu)	Recoverable Resources (Q Btu)	Remaining Resource Base (Q Btu)
Petroleum	1,550	3,680	14,400	60,000
Shale Oil	———	1,100	N/A	12,000,000
Tar Sands	.6	1,000	2,150	N/A
Natural Gas	670	1,860	15,800	32,000
Coal	3,340	N/A	N/A	340,000
Uranium				
Used in light-water reactors	N/A	510	990	650,000,000
Used in breeders	———	40,000	77,000	600 billion
Thorium used in breeders	———	22,000	66,000	N/A

Note: See note to Table 2 on the meaning of "Reserves," "Recoverable Resources," and "Remaining Resource Base."

Table 4. U.S. Production and Consumption of Energy, Selected Years, 1950–1973

Year	Coal (million short tons)		Petroleum (million barrels)		Natural Gas (billion cubic feet)		Total Energy (trillion Btu)	
	Produc-tion	Consump-tion	Produc-tion	Consump-tion*	Produc-tion*	Consump-tion**	Produc-tion	Consump-tion
1950	560.4	494.1	1,974	2,375	6,262	5,942	34,352	33,992
1955	490.8	447.0	2,484	3,100	9,405	8,920	39,082	39,703
1960	434.3	398.0	2,575	3,611	12,771	12,269	41,553	44,569
1965	527.0	472.1	2,849	4,202	16,040	15,598	49,074	53,343
1966	546.8	497.7	3,028	4,411	17,207	16,853	51,864	56,412
1967	564.9	491.2	3,216	4,585	18,171	17,685	54,829	58,265
1968.	556.7	509.0	3,329	4,902	19,322	18,973	56,575	61,763
1969	570.5	516.1	3,372	5,160	20,698	20,387	58,741	64,979
1970	612.6	523.9	3,517	5,365	21,921	21,367	61,852	67,143
1971	560.9	502.2	3,454	5,553	22,493	22,133	60,963	68,698
1972	596.5	525.7	3,455	5,990	22,532	22,429	62,277	72,108
1973	602.5	569.3	3,356	6,296	22,900	22,850	62,040	75,560

*—Includes natural gas liquids

**—Dry, excludes natural gas liquids

Source: U.S. Bureau of Mines

Table 5. Federal Energy R&D Funding Fiscal Year 1969 through Fiscal Year 1975 (in millions of dollars)

	FY 69	FY 70	FY 71	FY 72	FY 73	FY 74*	FY 75**
Coal Resource Development	$ 23.3	$ 30.4	$ 49.0	$ 76.8	$ 85.1	$164.4	$ 426.7
Petroleum and Natural Gas	13.5	14.8	17.5	23.8	18.7	19.1	41.8
Nuclear Fission							
LMFBR	132.5	144.3	167.9	237.4	253.7	357.3	473.4
Other Civilian Nuclear Power	144.6	109.1	97.7	90.7	152.8	173.2	251.7
Nuclear Fusion							
Magnetic Confinement	29.7	34.3	32.3	33.2	39.7	57.0	102.3
Laser-Pellet	2.1	3.2	9.3	14.0	35.1	44.1	66.3
Energy Conversion with Less							
Environmental Impact	12.3	22.9	22.8	33.4	38.4	65.5	178.5
General Energy R&D	3.0	4.2	8.7	15.4	8.1	28.8	59.8
Conservation including Transportation	N/A	N/A	N/A	N/A	32.2	65.0	115.7
Solar	N/A	N/A	N/A	N/A	4.0	13.8	50.0
Geothermal	N/A	N/A	N/A	N/A	4.4	10.9	44.7
	$361.0	$363.2	$405.2	$524.7	$672.2	$999.1	$1810.5

Note: Data for Fiscal Years 1969–1972 are not exactly comparable to Fiscal Years 1973–1975, as additional programs have been included.

Source: Executive Office of the President.

*Estimated

**Proposed

Table 6. World Petroleum Production and Reserves

	Production (in million barrels per day)				Reserves Jan. 1, 1974 (in billions of barrels)
	1971	1972	1973	Sept. 1973	
Middle East					
Abu Dhabi	0.9	1.0	1.3	1.4	21.5
Iran	4.5	4.9	6.0	5.9	60.0
Iraq	1.7	1.5	1.9	2.0	31.5
Kuwait	2.9	2.8	2.9	3.2	64.0
Saudi Arabia	4.5	5.7	7.4	8.3	132.0
Other		1.2	1.9		41.2
Total Middle East		17.6	21.4		350.2
Africa					
Algeria	0.8	1.1	1.0	1.1	7.6
Libya	2.8	2.2	2.1	2.3	25.5
Nigeria	1.5	1.8	2.0	2.0	20.0
Other		0.6	0.6		14.2
Total Africa		5.6	5.8		67.3
Asia-Pacific					
Indonesia	0.9	1.0	1.3		10.5
Other			0.9		5.1
Total Asia-Pacific			2.2		15.6
Europe			.4		16.0
Western Hemisphere					
U.S.	9.5	9.5	9.2		34.7
Canada	1.4	1.5	1.8		9.4
Venezuela	3.6	3.2	3.4		14.0
Other		1.3	1.8		17.7
Total Western Hemisphere		15.7	16.1		75.8
Communist Nations			9.3		103.0
Total World			55.2		627.9

Notes

Section 1

1. U.S. Department of the Interior, Bureau of Mines. Unless otherwise noted, all statistics on total U.S. energy use and on fuels production are from Bureau of Mines data.

2. Joel Darmstadter, "Appendix; Energy Consumption: Trends and Patterns," in Sam H. Schurr, ed., *Energy, Economic Growth, and the Environment,* Resources for the Future, John Hopkins Press, Baltimore, 1972.

3. William K. Reilly, ed., *The Use of Land; A Citizen's Policy Guide to Urban Growth,* Rockefeller Brothers Fund, Thomas Y. Crowell Co., New York, 1973.

4. Washington Center for Metropolitan Studies, preliminary work on energy and lifestyles, draft report in preparation for the Energy Policy Project. Unless otherwise noted, statistics on residential energy use are derived from a national survey conducted for WCMS by Response Analysis, Inc., during the winter and spring of 1972–73.

5. Richard G. Stein, "Architecture and Energy," *Forum,* July/August 1973.

6. The Energy Policy Project has commissioned a study of "Energy Conservation Opportunities in Building Design" by the American Institute of Architects Research Corporation. Also relevant to commercial energy conservation is an EPP-sponsored study of "Institutional Problems of the Application of New Community Energy Systems Technologies," being conducted at the Environmental Quality Labratory of California Institute of Technology. This study considers the problems inherent in translating research and development into widespread commercial application of solar systems, total energy systems and fuel cells.

7. Washington Center for Metropolitan Studies, preliminary work on energy and lifestyles.

8. Motor Vehicle Manufacturers Association, *Automobile Facts and Figures,* 1972.

9. Eric Hirst, *Energy Intensiveness of Passenger and Freight Transport Modes, 1950–1970,* Oak Ridge National Laboratory, April, 1973. Subsequent data on transportation traffic energy use and energy-intensiveness are also from Hirst, unless otherwise noted.

10. Remarks of John C. Sawhill, Deputy Administrator of the Federal Energy Office, before the National Association of Automobile Dealers, Las Vegas, Nevada, February 5, 1974.

11. Environmental Protection Agency, Office of Air and Water Programs, "Fuel Economy and Emission Control," November 1972.

12. Sawhill remarks.

13. U.S. Environmental Protection Agency, "EPA's Position in the Energy Crisis," *Environmental News,* January 1974.

14. Stanford Research Institute, *Patterns of Energy Consumption in the United States,* prepared for the Office of Science and Technology, Executive Office of the President, Government Printing Office, Washington, 1972. See Table 1.

15. The Energy Policy Project has sponsored two studies of energy use in industry. The Conference Board has looked at patterns of energy use in the highly energy-consumptive industries over the last decade and at prospects for future conservation in these industries. Economic and technological factors are both considered in the Conference Board study of "Energy Consumption in Manufacturing." A second study, Lazarus Lazarides, "Potential for Fuel Conservation in Industry," Thermo Electron Corporation, focuses on specific technological innovations for energy conservation in the energy-intensive industries.

16. Conference Board, "Energy Consumption in Manufacturing," Volume I, Summary.

17. U.S. Department of Commerce, Bureau of the Census, *Statistical Abstract of the United States, 1972,* Government Printing Office, Washington, 1972.

18. U.S. Bureau of Mines.

19. U.S. Bureau of the Census, *Statistical Abstract.*

20. U.S. Bureau of Mines.

21. Morgan Stanley & Co., "Energy Outlook," New York, December 12, 1973.

22. John Lichtblau, "Needed: More Refineries, *New York Times,* July 29, 1973.

23. U.S. Bureau of Mines.

24. National Coal Association, *Bituminous Coal Facts 1972.*

25. National Coal Association, *Bituminous Coal Data,* 1972 Edition.
26. Hirst, *Energy Intensiveness of Transport Modes.*

Section 2

1. The subject is considered in Thomas D. Duchesneau, "Competition in the Energy Industry," draft report to the Energy Policy Project.
2. A discussion of R&D policy is the subject of draft report to the EPP, Herbert J. Holloman et al., "Energy R&D Proposals," Massachusetts Institute of Technology, Center for Policy Alternatives.
3. National Resources Defense Council, "Government Decisionmaking Papers, draft reports to the EPP.

Section 3

1. The Brookings Institution, "International Aspects of Energy Policy," draft report to the Energy Policy Project.
2. *International Economic Report of the President,* Government Printing Office, Washington, 1974.
3. "Shock for the Third World," *The Petroleum Economist,* February, 1974.
4. Mason Willrich and Theodore B. Taylor, *Nuclear Theft: Risks and Safeguards,* Ballinger Publishing Company, Cambridge, April, 1974.
5. Donald F. Boesch and Carl H. Hershner, "The Ecological Effects of Oil Pollution in the Marine Environment," draft report to the Energy Policy Project.

Section 4

1. Marc Ross et al., "Energy Costs of Limiting the Degradation of the Environment," University of Michigan, draft report to the Energy Policy Project.
2. L. B. Barrett and T. E. Waddell, "Cost of Air Pollution Damage: A Status Report," Environmental Protection Agency, February, 1973.
3. Update of Reference 2, to be published in 1974 by EPA.
4. "A Review of the Health Effects of Sulfur Oxides," submitted to the Office of Management and Budget by D. P. Rall, National Institute of Environmental Health Sciences, National Institutes of Health, October 9, 1973.
5. J. F. Finklea, "Conceptual Basis for Establishing Standards," *Proceedings on the Conference on Health Effects of Air Pollutants,* Assembly of Life Sciences, National Academy of Sciences/National Research Council, October 3–5, 1973. Prepared for the Committee on Public Works of the U.S. Senate, November, 1973.
6. "The Potential for Energy Conservation: Substitution for Scarce Fuels," Office of Emergency Preparedness, January, 1973.
7. B. W. Carnow et al., "Health Effects of Energy Systems," draft report to the Energy Policy Project from the American Public Health Association.

8. S. K. Friedlander, "Small Particles in Air Pose a Big Control Problem," *Environmental Science and Technology,* vol. 7, number 13, p. 1115, December, 1973.

9. D. F. S. Natush et al., "Toxic Trace Elements: Preferential Concentration in Respirable Particles," *Science,* vol. 183, January 18, 1974.

10. K. T. Whitby, Department of Mechanical Engineering, University of Minnesota, personal communication.

11. "Abatement of Particulate Emissions from Stationary Sources," National Academy of Engineering, 1972.

12. "Environmental News," Environmental Protection Agency, January, 1974.

13. "Session 3, Nitrogen Oxides," *Proceedings of the Conference on Health Effects of Air Pollutants,* cited in Note 5.

14. E. A. Nephew, "The Challenge and Promise of Coal," *Technology Review,* December, 1973.

15. "Coal Surface Mining and Reclamation," Council on Environmental Quality, Executive Office of the President, March, 1973.

16. "Surface Mining of Coal," Special Report No. 6, Investor Responsibility Research Center, Washington, D.C., October 29, 1973.

17. Thadis W. Box et al., National Academy of Sciences, *Rehabilitation Potential of Western Coal Lands,* Ballinger Publishing Company, Cambridge, May, 1974.

18. Water Resources Work Group, Northern Great Plains Resources Program (work in progress; anticipated preliminary report, June, 1974).

19. Vernon E. Swanson, U.S. Geological Survey, personal communication.

20. C. E. Capes et al, "Rejection of Trace Metals from Coal during Benefication by Agglomeration," *Environmental Science and Technology,* vol. 8, No. 1, p. 35, January, 1974.

21. "Acid Mine Drainage in Appalachia," A Report by the Appalachian Regional Commission, 1969.

22. D. E. Kash et al, *Energy Under the Ocean,* University of Oklahoma Press, Norman, 1973.

23. Donald F. Boesch and Carl H. Hershner, "The Ecological Effects of Oil Pollution in the Marine Environment," draft report to the EPP.

24. Jerome H. Milgram, "Technological Aspects of the Prevention Control and Cleanup of Oil Spills in the Ocean," Massachusetts Institute of Technology, Department of Ocean Engineering, draft report to the EPP.

25. U.S. Department of the Interior, *Final Environmental Statement for the Prototype Oil Shale Leasing Program,* Government Printing Office, Washington, 1973.

26. P. K. Theobold et al., "Energy Resources of the United States," U.S. Geological Survey Circular 650, Washington, 1972.

27. G. Yadigaroglu et al., "Spent Fuel Transportation Risks," *Nuclear News*, p. 71, November, 1974.

28. Marc Ross, "The Possibility of Release of Cesium in a Spent-Fuel Transportation Accident," University of Michigan Physics Department, January, 1974.

29. A. S. Kubo and D. J. Rose, "Nuclear Waste Disposal," *Science*, p. 1205, December 21, 1973.

30. T. C. Hollocher, "Storage and Disposal of High Level Wastes," in *The Nuclear Fuel Cycle*, Union of Concerned Scientists, October, 1973.

31. Mason Willrich and Theodore B. Taylor, *Nuclear Theft: Risks and Safeguards*, Ballinger Publishing Company, Cambridge, April, 1974.

32. "Dixie Lee Ray Provides Some Details of Rasmussen Study on Nuclear Accidents," *Weekly Energy Report*, January 28, 1974.

33. "Study of Quality Verification and Budget Impact," Task Force Report to the Director of Regulation, U.S. Atomic Energy Commission, January, 1974.

34. D. F. Ford and H. W. Kendall, "Catastrophic Nuclear Accidents," in *The Nuclear Fuel Cycle*, Union of Concerned Scientists, October, 1973.

35. A. M. Weinberg, "Social Institutions and Nuclear Energy," *Science*, July 7, 1972.

36. A. V. Kneese, "The Faustian Bargain," *Resources*, Resources for the Future, September, 1973.

37. Hannes Alfven, "Energy and Environment," *Bulletin of the Atomic Scientists*, May, 1972.

Section 5

1. Thadis W. Box, National Academy of Sciences, *Rehabilitation Potential of Western Coal Lands*, Ballinger Publishing Company, Cambridge, May, 1974.

Section 6

1. Herbert Hollomon et al., "Energy R&D Policy Proposals," Massachusetts Institute of Technology, Center for Policy Alternatives, draft report to the Energy Policy Project.

2. Gerard M. Brannon, "The Role of Taxes and Subsidies in United States Energy Policy," draft report to the EPP.

3. Jerome Hass et al, "Capital Expenditures and Financial Requirements of the Energy Industries," draft report to the EPP.

4. Washington Center for Metropolitan Studies, preliminary work on energy and lifestyles, draft report in preparation for the EPP.

5. K. J. Saulter, "Energy, Employment, and the Economy," EPP draft staff report.

Section 7

1. U.S. Bureau of the Census Series E, December, 1972, which projects a U.S. population of 236 million in 1935 and 265 million in 2000.

2. Sam H. Schurr et al., "Supply Reports," Resources for the Future, draft report to the Energy Policy Project.

3. M. K. Hubbert, "Energy Resources," *Resources and Man*, Committee on Resources and Man, National Academy of Sciences/National Research Council, W. H. Freeman and Company, San Francisco, 1969.

4. Jerome Hass et al., "The Capital Expenditures and Financial Requirements of the Energy Industry," draft report to the EPP.

5. Jerome Weingart, Richard Schoen et al., "Institutional Problems of the Application of New Community Energy Systems Technologies," Caltech Environmental Quality Laboratory, draft report to the EPP.

6. Lazarus Lazarides et al., "Potential for Fuel Conservation in Industry," Thermo-Electron Corporation, draft report to the EPP.

7. "Michigan Pushes Home Insulation," *New York Times*, August 26, 1973.

8. D. L. Meadows et al., *The Limits to Growth*, Universe Books, New York, 1972.

9. "Blueprint for Survival," *The Ecologist*, January, 1972.

10. H. E. Daly, ed., *Toward a Steady State Economy*, W. H. Freeman and Company, San Francisco, 1973.

11. "The No-Growth Society," *Daedalus*, Journal of the American Academy of Arts and Sciences, vol. 102, No. 4, Fall, 1973.

12. Massachusetts Institute of Technology Seminar on Strategies for Sustainable Growth, January 17–18, 1974.

13. R. L. Heilbroner, "The Human Prospect," *The New York Review*, January 24, 1974.

14. Daniel Bell, *The Coming of the Post Industrial Society*, Basic Books, New York, 1973.

15. *Inadvertent Climate Modification*, Report of the Study of Man's Impact on Climate, Massachusetts Institute of Technology Press, Cambridge, 1971.

16. M. I. Budyko, *Climate and Life*, Hydrological Publishing House, Leningrad, 1971.

17. S. Manabe, "Estimates of Future Change of Climate Due to the Increase of Carbon Dioxide Concentration in the Air," in W. H. Matthews et al., ed., *Man's Impact on the Climate*, Massachusetts Institute of Technology Press, Cambridge, 1971.

PLEASE NOTE:

Readers of this volume who are interested in learning more about the findings of the Ford Foundation's Energy Policy Project, may wish to acquire the recently completed final report of the Project. This 510-page volume, entitled *A Time to Choose: America's Energy Future,* sets forth in greater detail the results of the Project's comprehensive two-year analysis of energy issues, and makes recommendations for a national energy policy.

Priced at $10.95 in a cloth covered edition and at $3.95 in paper, copies may be obtained at bookstores or by sending a check or money order to Ballinger Publishing Company, 17 Dunster Street, Harvard Square, Cambridge, Massachusetts 02138.

The Project has also sponsored publication of a multi-volume series of research reports, which it commissioned from independent experts in the energy field. Ballinger Publishing Company will be happy to send upon request further information about this series.